Introduction  re

Introduction to Computer Architecture

Introduction
to Computer Architecture

Neil Willis
and **Jon Kerridge**

Department of Computer Studies
Sheffield City Polytechnic

PITMAN PUBLISHING
128 Long Acre, London WC2E 9AN

A Division of Longman Group UK Limited

© Neil Willis and Jon Kerridge 1983

First published in Great Britain 1983
Reprinted 1984, 1986, 1988, 1989, 1991, 1992

British Library Cataloguing in Publication Data
Willis, Neil
  Introduction to computer architecture.
  1. Electronic digital computers
  I. Title   II. Kerridge, Jon
  001.64   QA76.5

ISBN 0–273–01438–2

Printed and bound in Singapore

Contents

Preface

The aim of this book is to provide a student text which presents the ideas and concepts of computer architecture in a well organized and straightforward manner. It develops the fundamental concepts from the register transfer level upwards, not concerning itself with the logic level at all.

It does not assume any prerequisite knowledge of computers although we feel that the material is best taught in parallel with a course in assembler level or machine code programming. Indeed, the assembler level programming might well form the practical or tutorial part of such a course. Such practical sessions will certainly reinforce the understanding of Chapters 4, 5, 6, 7 and 8.

The choice of an illustrative computer for a text such as this is a much debated topic. Our basic premise is that to use examples of real machines is ideal and consequently examples are taken throughout the text from a variety of machines such as an IBM 370, PDP-11, ICL 2900, Hewlett Packard 2000 and HP 3000, Prime 750, Harris 800 and Motorola M6800.

These examples will complement the lecturer's illustrations of facilities available on the computer being used for the practical work.

However, if it is not possible to illustrate a particular technique on the computer available, Appendix 2 of the text describes a computer system simulator. This is a software package written in Pascal and is available to lecturers who would like to use it, at a nominal materials charge. Some of the problems in the text relate to the use of the simulator although they can obviously be solved on a real computer.

The general structure of the book is as follows. Chapter 1 introduces all the basic concepts of computing systems giving definitions of processors, memory, peripherals, backing store, communications and distributed systems. Because a distributed system is a collection of single processors, this topic is discussed further in Chapter 9 after the details of a single processor system have been described.

Chapter 2 introduces descriptions of basic peripheral devices and gives the reader an appreciation of the physical characteristics, relative costs and flexibility of a wide range of peripheral devices.

Chapter 3 describes a range of backing store devices such as magnetic disc, drum, tape, floppy disc, bubble store, charge couple devices, content addressable file store.

Chapter 4 provides a functional description of memory together with a brief description of the technologies used to implement memory. The functional description includes interleaving and associative techniques as well as the Von Neumann structure.

Chapter 5 gives an outline of the structure and requirements of machine code and a review of addressing techniques.

Chapter 6 is a functional description of a processing unit including synchronous and asynchronous operation. Discussion of information flow in the processing unit leads naturally to the requirements for micro instructions and to descriptions of hardware and software micro instruction techniques.

Chapter 7 introduces the need for interrupts and discusses situations in which they may occur. A review of interrupt handling techniques follows.

Chapter 8 is concerned with the transfer of information to and from peripheral devices. As well as input/output to 'close' devices the chapter includes a review of data transmission techniques.

Chapter 9 shows how computers may be linked to form a distributed system, from both the hardware and software aspects.

Chapter 10 describes architectural developments which have been used to increase processor throughput.

Appendix 1 is a brief description of binary, octal, decimal and hexadecimal number systems. It describes the representation of characters and fixed and floating point numbers.

Appendix 2 is a specification of a computer system simulator together with a number of systems which can be used for teaching purposes.

This book has been based on a lecture course forming part of a BSc in Computer Studies and much of the text and many of the problems have been 'class tested'. We are very grateful to many students who have commented on their difficulties and for suggestions they have made for improvements to the material.

We also wish to express our thanks to all the people who have helped during the preparation of this book. In particular we are very grateful to Dan Simpson for his contribution of Chapter 9 and to Doug Bell for his patient reading of the entire text and his detailed and very helpful comments and suggestions.

Finally we wish to thank Mrs J M Kerridge and Mrs M Wilson for their very careful typing.

Neil Willis
Jon Kerridge
Sheffield, 1982

1 Basic concepts of computer systems

Computer systems are constructed from many different component parts and by connecting these parts together in different ways computer systems with different facilities can be built. However, there is within this variation much that is common. This chapter introduces you to the basic concepts that are common to all computing machines. Having acquired this fundamental knowledge you will then be able to go on and expand upon the framework provided.

1.1 Computing machines and computer systems

The first computing machines were built in the late 1940s. In retrospect they were somewhat limited in that they were designed to solve one particular problem or a small class of problems. Throughout the 1950s and 1960s developments were made which allowed the same computing machine to be used for many different classes of problem. During this time there were technological changes from the valve to the transistor which allowed more complex and more reliable computing machines to be built. It was also during this period that software was developed which opened up the use of the computer to the less specialized users. This was achieved by using programming languages which did not require the user to have intimate knowledge of the construction of the computing machine. There were also developed software systems which made the computing machine more flexible and this gave rise to the term computer system.

During the 1970s there were large developments in the electronics technology industry. These developments enabled the price of computing machines to fall dramatically. Together this meant that it was possible to build computer systems which were constructed from more than one computing machine.

1.1.1 *What is a computing machine?*

A computing machine is a piece of electronic equipment which, when given some data will process that data in some pre-defined way to produce the required results. It is fundamental to the concept that the operations which

1

take place do so in a finite time. A computing machine requires some means of accepting data, somewhere to store the sequence of operations to be carried out, some means of performing the calculations required and finally a method of communicating the results. These facilities are common to any computing machine regardless of the task to which it will be put.

1.1.2 *The difference between computing machines and computer systems*

A computer system takes the basic computing machine and by the addition of software makes the computer system more flexible so that it can be used to solve many different types of problem.

In the simplest case there is a one to one correspondence between a computing machine and a computer system. That is, the computer system uses only one computing machine.

However, the tendency is to develop computer systems that consist of several computing machines. There are two important reasons for this. Firstly, the nature of the environment—may best be supported by providing many localized computing machines—which also provide flexibility by communicating with each other. Secondly, there may be a security aspect which requires certain information held by the computer system to be maintained separate from other parts of the system. Such systems are called distributed systems. An example of such an environment is provided by a medical information system for a hospital. Each ward requires rapid information about patients on that ward but when a patient is moved within the hospital the information relating to that patient should still be available. Also by distributing patient information it is inherently more secure.

These variations of requirement arise, for example, when many computing machines form a computer system but where some of the machines are general purpose and others are dedicated machines.

A general purpose computing machine is one which can be used to solve many types of problem. A dedicated computer is one used for one task only: for example, controlling a process in manufacturing industry. In a computer system constructed from such components the general purpose computing machines could be used to extract information maintained by the dedicated machine.

A dedicated computing machine is the same as a general purpose machine in its fundamental construction. It is only dedicated by the connections made between it and the environment in which it operates. An illustration would be a computerized railway system where there will be specialized sensors able to detect the presence of a train and others to check that a set of points have moved as well as the electronically controlled equipment which moves the points. The computer which controls such a system will be dedicated to the task of controlling the movement of trains and will not be used for any other task. These specialized sensors and the equipment which causes mechanical operations to take place are called transducers.

1.2 Basic components of a computing machine

Computing machines, whether dedicated or general purpose can be represented by the following block diagram (Fig. 1.1). Obviously in

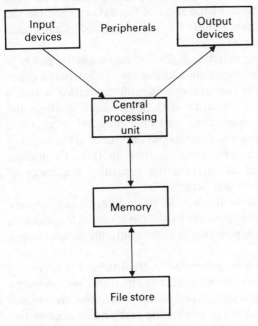

Fig. 1.1

particular instances some of the components may assume greater importance.

1.2.1 *Central processing unit*

The central processing unit (CPU) provides central control of the functions of the whole computing machine. In order to function correctly a computing machine requires all necessary data to be made available to the component parts of the machine at exactly the right time. If this is not done the user of the computing machine would find that the results produced by the computing machine would be wrong. As well as providing control functions the CPU also provides the arithmetic and logic capability of the computing machine.

1.2.2 *Memory*

The memory of a computing machine is used to hold two distinct types of information: first the data which is to be processed by the computing machine and secondly, the finite sequence of operations which will process that data to produce desired results. The sequence of operations is called an algorithm. The algorithm is said to operate upon a data structure, the data structure being a description of the form of the data rather than the particular data values. The combination of an algorithm and its associated data structure is called a program.

The memory of a computing machine is divided into many similar cells or locations each of which is individually addressable. To say that a cell is addressable means that a CPU can uniquely identify a location within a program so that it can hold a specified data item value. Similarly the address can be used by the algorithmic part of a program to alter the sequence of execution of operations. Instructions are stored in the memory of the computer in sequence, one location after another. Computing machines are extremely good at carrying out repetitive sequences of operations because they are fast and accurate.

This situation is very similar to the way in which knitting patterns are described. The knitter is told the sequence of stitches required to produce a desired effect and then told to repeat that sequence until the desired length has been achieved.

In order that repetitions can be generated in algorithms it is necessary for the sequence to be able to go back over itself, thus generating the necessary repetitions. The addresses of the memory locations are utilized by some of the operations within the computing machine to achieve this effect.

Most memories are unable to distinguish from the contents of a location whether it contains data, algorithm or irrelevant information. It is up to the user of a computer to ensure that appropriate locations of the memory are filled with sensible data and an algorithm before commencing any processing.

1.2.3 *File store*

The file store holds bulk data and its storage capacity is very large. A single unit of file store may contain ten or a hundred times more locations than the memory itself. The file store can then be constructed from many such units. In order that this large amount of storage space can be more easily managed it is logically split into smaller sections called files. It is then usual to associate some of the files with a particular program. However, in most computer systems there is nothing to stop any file being processed by any program provided the data is stored in the correct format according to the data structure in the program.

Memory is one of the more expensive components of a computer and it is, therefore, not an infinite resource. Hence, within one computing machine it would not take long before the memory was filled by programs which although required were not currently being executed. The file store provides a means of keeping copies of these programs available to the computing machine in a state of readiness. When such a stored program is required it can be brought from the file store and placed in memory so that it can be executed. On completion, the program will be returned to the file store until required again.

Probably a more important use of file store is for the recording of bulk data. The program describes the data structure upon which it will operate but not the actual data values to be manipulated. These data values have to be stored somewhere and presented to the algorithm as required. In the majority of data processing applications there is far too much data to be processed for it all to be in the memory at the same time. This bulk data is stored in the file store and then transferred to the program as necessary.

It is usual to have a means of identifying users of the computer system so that only those with appropriate authorization can process specific data files with particular programs.

1.2.4 *Peripherals*

The majority of data processed by a computer together with the algorithms has to be placed in the computer by some method of communication. A peripheral provides this communication with the outside world.

Peripherals can be divided into three classes; input devices, output devices and i/o devices which are capable of communicating in both modes. In a general purpose computer system there will be many different peripherals, so that the user has a degree of flexibility and the use of peripherals is thus tailored to the needs of the application.

In a dedicated computer system it is often the peripherals which make the system dedicated. Up to this stage the computer could have been used for many different applications. The connection of certain peripherals in the form of specific transducers dedicates the computer system. Such dedication is found in process control.

In this case the computer system has to be able to respond rapidly to the requirements of the process being controlled. It would not be sufficient for this data to be transferred by a human operator. Thus it is necessary for the information collected from the parameter being sensed to be entered directly into the computer.

1.3 Putting it all together

Up to this stage it may have appeared that the only place for variation in computing machines and computer systems is in the nature of peripherals and in the amount of memory and file store available. This is not the case and it is the role of the computer architect to design a computing machine so that it will best respond to the environment in which it will be used. To this end, the computer architect has to make a great many decisions about the way in which the basic building blocks will be constructed and then how they will be connected together to form a unified solution for the problem environment. There is no one correct solution for a single environment because each architect has his own ideas and there is usually a financial compromise to be taken into account. Hence, given the same initial building blocks, it is possible to construct many different computing machines, some of which will be more appropriate to particular areas.

We will discuss briefly some of these design criteria at this stage but they will be expanded upon in later chapters.

1.3.1 *Interconnection*

The architect or designer has initially many ways in which he can connect the component parts of the computer together. By incorporating a large number of specific connections he can make the computing machine process extremely quickly. This approach is, however, costly because it requires a lot of expensive electronic components.

Conversely the components of the computer can be connected together in a far more generalized way which saves on component costs, as not so many are used. In that event the computer system will process information more slowly because it is typical of such systems that the same components are used for many different data transfers. Hence some transfers may have to wait until a previous transfer has been completed. It is thus the job of the architect to choose the right compromise between speed and cost so that the computer system satisfies its design criteria.

1.3.2 *Operating systems*

Besides producing the computing machine a computer manufacturer usually provides some means of controlling the complete computer system. In very small systems this may be left to the purchaser. The computing system control mechanism is provided by means of a program called the operating system. The operating system is a program always available to the computer. It allows the computing machine to be operated at maximum efficiency within a system related to a particular environment.

A computer system provides the user with three basic resources namely, processing time, memory to store algorithms and data, and finally use of peripherals. One measure of operating system efficiency is to see how effectively it manages these resources so as to ensure that each resource is used to the maximum. One way is to keep several programs simultaneously in a partial state of execution within the computer. Each is given a share of the machine in turn. Obviously this requires a very complex operating system. Such an operating system will maintain a list of programs waiting to be executed for the first time. From this list the operating system will select that program which allows it to make most effective use of the resources.

An alternative approach is to initiate a program and then let it execute until processing is completed. This will obviously be wasteful of resources, but the operating system will be much simpler and quicker in operation.

The computer architect has to be aware of the sort of operating system to be used with the computing machine. He has, therefore, to design the computing machine and take account of the operating system. It is possibly true to say that there is more cost involved in the analysis, design and implementation of the operating system than there is of the underlying computing machine. Hence the computing machine and the operating system are normally designed in parallel.

1.3.3 *Distribution*

Increasingly the computer architect has had to become more aware of the problems caused by distributed computer systems.

As explained earlier, a distributed computer system is one which is constructed from several computing machines. Each of the computing machines needs to communicate with its immediate neighbours in the system. So that this may be done in an orderly fashion facilities have to be provided either by programs within the operating system or by the CPUs of the machines. Such facilities are called protocols.

If copies of the same data are stored on several different computing machines then there has to be a mechanism to ensure that all copies have been updated before any user has access to any copy of the data.

Another major problem arises when deciding what facilities of the computer system are to be distributed. The facilities to be considered are processing capability and data storage. The spectrum ranges from a distributed system which has a central file store with many computing machines connected, to a system which has processing and data storage capabilities uniformly distributed.

The computer architect has to ensure that either he constructs computing machines that can operate in all these modes or a range of computing machines each of which is suited to a particular role within the distributed system.

1.4 Summary

This chapter has introduced the underlying concepts of computing machines and computer systems. These underlying concepts will be enlarged upon in subsequent chapters. Finally in Chapter 9 we expand further the concept of a computer system as a collection of computing machines.

2 Peripherals

Chapter 1 introduced the concept of a computing machine being able to process data that has been presented to it in some way and of the computing machine presenting the results of its processing back to the outside world. The parts of the computing machine which are involved in the transfer of data to and from the outside world are known as peripheral devices and can be categorized as follows.

(a) Input   devices used to transfer information *into* the computing machine,

(b) Output   devices used to transfer information *out* from the computing machine to the outside world,

(c) Input/ output   devices which can be used for both the input or the output of data,

(d) Television technology   these are currently available methods of data transmission based on television,

(e) Specific transducers   devices which will sense such things as pressure, temperature etc. and pass information directly into the computer.

Within any one of these classes there may be devices of a similar type, some which may be used as peripheral devices to a small computer and some as peripheral devices to a much larger computing machine. The differences in the devices lie in their ruggedness, capacity, speed and cost. Clearly, devices intended to accompany a small portable computer will have to be smaller and lighter than similar devices which are permanently attached to a large, static, general purpose computer. In achieving the smaller size and lighter weight (and often lower cost), ruggedness, capacity and speed may have to be sacrificed.

2.1 Input peripherals

As indicated later, in Chapters 4 and 8, information can be stored in character form in the main memory of a computing machine by using some appropriate numeric code. The purpose of an input peripheral is to transfer information from its real world representation into the internal character code of the computing machine. Because information in the real world exists in many different formats, several different input devices may be used under different circumstances.

2.1.1 *Paper tape input*

Information is represented in a machine readable form as a pattern of holes across the width of a strip of paper tape. The tape itself is typically one inch wide, successive characters being represented by a pattern of up to eight holes at a spacing of ten characters to the inch.

The tape is prepared by someone typing on the keyboard of a machine known as a paper tape punch. When all the tape has been prepared (and this usually involves a verification process to check that the correct data has been punched) the information on the tape can be 'read' by a peripheral device known as a paper tape reader. Paper tape readers appear to read the data very quickly, and speeds of up to 2000 characters per second are not uncommon. But by comparison with the speed at which the central processing unit can process instructions (see Chapter 6) they are in fact relatively slow. The paper tape reader works on the following principle. Rollers grip the tape and when they spin rapidly the tape is fed through the reader. A beam of light is shone down on to the tape at right angles to the direction of travel. Underneath the tape are a series of eight photoelectric cells, one in each of the eight hole positions. When a particular character passes through the beam of light, the light passes through the hole and activates the photoelectric cell which will release a pulse of electricity. Where there is no hole, the light will not pass through and activate the cell. Thus the character which was first translated into a pattern of holes is now translated into a unique pattern of electronic pulses.

Here are some of the advantages and disadvantages of paper tape.

Advantages	*Disadvantages*
1 Cheapness. Reels of paper tape are fairly inexpensive.	1 Difficult to 'read' by human beings.
2 Compactness. A 5-inch diameter reel of tape may be able to hold 120 000 characters of information.	2 Correcting punched data is difficult and usually involves copying the whole tape.
3 Items of information may be of variable length (cf. punched cards).	3 Needs rewinding after being read, if it is to be retained.

Advantages

4 It can be produced as a by-product of keyboard machines such as cash registers, although magnetic storage devices are now much more common.

5 Paper tape uses the Universal ASCII code (see Section 8.7.4).

2.1.2 *Punched cards*

Punched cards have been used for storing data since the end of the last century. For many years mechanical and electro-mechanical machines were in use which accepted data from cards into which holes had been punched according to a set code. They also did simple additions and subtractions of numeric items.

The standard present day punched card is a piece of thin cardboard measuring $7\frac{3}{8}$ inches $\times 3\frac{1}{4}$ inches. It is divided horizontally into 12 rows and vertically into 80 columns. A particular character is represented by a unique pattern of holes punched into one column.

As with paper tape, the cards are prepared by someone typing on the keyboard of a machine known as a card punch. Again there will be a verification process needed (this usually involves punching all the data again) to ensure that the information that has been punched is correct, and the 'deck' of cards can then be read into the computer by a peripheral device known as a card reader, which works on a similar principle to the paper tape reader. Cards can be read at speeds of up to 30 cards per second although if all 80 columns of a card are not used to contain useful data (and in practice this is usually the case) the number of useful characters read per second will be much less, since it takes the same amount of time for a card to pass through the card reader regardless of the number of columns that actually contain characters.

Below are some of the advantages and disadvantages of punched cards:

Advantages	*Disadvantages*
1 Card codes are universal.	1 Rarely are all card columns used.
2 A card may be easily added to, inserted, removed or replaced from a 'deck' of cards.	2 A card reader is a relatively slow input device.
3 Cards may be processed off-line (that is on machines not connected to the computer) e.g. sorted, merged, collated, reproduced.	3 Requires verification—additional equipment.

Advantages	*Disadvantages*
4 A card may be a source document, e.g. clock card, prepunched card.	4 It is relatively expensive.

There are a number of special applications for which cards are useful. in some applications it is advantageous to have a computer to output information on punched cards and so avoid the lengthy data preparation process and errors, the cards being used as input media in a further data processing run. A good example of this is shoe sales statistics. The prepunched card is packed in the shoe box and when the retail outlet sells the shoes the card is returned to the manufacturer (or perhaps to the retailer's central warehouse) where an analysis of the sales trends is made.

Another use of prepunched cards (although not the standard size punched card) is that of the Kimball tags. These are small cards on which precoded information is punched. They are used mainly in the retail, particularly garment, trade and contain data about an item of goods. They are detached and returned to a central statistical collecting point as the goods are sold.

2.1.3 *Key to tape/disk*

This form of input device was developed to eliminate some of the disadvantages of input via paper tape or punched cards. The data is keyed in at a keyboard but is stored initially in the electronic memory, thus allowing for easy correction. If the operator realizes that a character has been miskeyed, the backspace is depressed, the correct character keyed in, and the memory's stored character is corrected. Once all the characters in the record (a record being a convenient collection of characters—see Chapter 3) are keyed in, the record can then be recorded on the magnetic tape or disk (see Chapter 3).

The main advantages are:

1 Increased productivity of punch/keyboard operators, because of the ease of error correction;
2 Some automatic error checking can be built into the system;
3 There is a ready visual check on the small TV screen (VDU);
4 No expendable materials;
5 The tape/disk thus produced provides a much faster read in to the computer system compared with punched cards or paper tape.

2.1.4 *Point of sale (POS) systems*

Recent advances in technology, in particular the microprocessor, have led to the development of point of sale devices, primarily for use in shops. The collection of data at the point of sale has been accepted for many years;

Kimball tags, prepunched cards and by-product paper tape have been widely used in the retail trade. However, the introduction of micro-processors and low cost keyboard/display devices have led to a number of variations of this equipment, the most common being electronic cash registers and cash terminals.

Electronic cash registers These are small computers with keyboard and simple display facilities to show price data. The cashier keys in an item identifier and price (although prices may be held in a memory). The cash register accumulates sales under a range of nominated codes for subsequent processing. Data may be collected on cassette tapes (see Chapter 3).

Cash terminals These are usually connected to a small computer in the store. This central computer controls a network of terminals at pay-points, and has stock and price data usually stored on disks. The terminal is used to input details of each sale made. A common method of identifying items is by passing a magnetic/optical sensing wand over a tag on each item. Items are priced automatically and receipts printed on the terminal. Stock sales data is accumulated for later processing leading to automatic reordering.

2.1.5 *Optical character recognition (OCR)*

Devices are available that, by a process of optically scanning documents, are able to recognize character shapes. They may be capable of reading whole pages (page reader) or merely one or two lines only. Generally, the characters to be read must be machine printed and of a special character design or fount. In America, a character fount known as OCR 'A' has evolved while in Europe OCR 'B' has been developed. Figure 2.1 illustrates both these founts.

Below are some of the advantages and disadvantages of OCR.

Advantages	*Disadvantages*
1 Computers can produce pre-printed documents which can later be read.	1 Documents must be treated with care.
2 Data preparation errors are eliminated.	2 Special measures are required to replace spoilt or lost documents.
3 Document is a visible record.	3 Equipment is very expensive.
4 Considerable range of document size is catered for.	4 Print quality may be critical.
5 Can be on line to the computer (but often data written to magnetic tape off line for faster computer input).	

OCR 'A' fount

A B C D E F G H a b c d e f g h
I J K L M N O P i j k l m n o p
Q R S T U V W X q r s t u v w x
Y Z * + , − . / y z m å ø æ
0 1 2 3 4 5 6 7 £ $: ; < % > ?
8 9   [@ ! # & ,]
          (=) ¨ ´ ^ ~ ˇ
Ä ö Å Ñ Ü Æ Ø ↑ ≤ ≥ × ÷ o ¤

OCR 'B' fount

0 1 2 3 4 5 6 7 8 9 ⑈⑆⑇⑉

MICR E13B fount

Fig. 2.1

2.1.6 *Magnetic ink character recognition (MICR)*

In MICR specially designed characters are used which are printed in ink containing magnetic particles. The document is read by a document reader that recognizes the particular character from the variation in magnetic flux which is induced by the shape of that particular character.

Banks are the main users of this system. By preprinting the cheque serial number, the bank and branch sorting code numbers, and the customer's account number in a single line along the bottom of cheques before issue, it is possible to sort the cheques, after they have been presented, by means of a MICR sorting machine. The amount of the cheque is encoded on the cheque in MICR fount by a keyboard machine called a magnetic ink encoder. The cheques are then read by the magnetic ink character reader which can verify the characters and then send the data directly to the computer or to magnetic tape or disk for later input to the computer.

Figure 2.1 illustrates the fount known as E 13 B, that is common to the banking world in both America and the United Kingdom.

Below are some of the advantages and disadvantages of MICR.

Advantages	*Disadvantages*
1 Visual inspection possible with practice.	1 One line of information per document only.
2 Useful for document sorting.	2 Cannot be produced by computer; printing requires special printing device.
3 Forgery impeded.	3 The quality of printing is important, the amount of ink in a character is critical.
	4 Very limited character set in E 13 B.

2.2 Output peripherals

The purpose of an output peripheral is to transfer information from its internal character code as stored inside the computing machine to an appropriate real world representation. This real world representation may be a printed page, a television tube, a diagram on paper, magnetic spots on plastic tape or even microfiche.

Society as a whole is very much geared to the use of the printed word and consequently the most common forms of output device are those which produce printed information on paper, commonly referred to as 'hard copy'. There are now a number of different types of printing device. Some printers operate like typewriters in that type strikes an inked ribbon which in turn strikes paper to transfer an image. These are known as impact printers. More recent innovations have brought about the printing of characters by heat, ink jet and photography, known generally as nonimpact printers. The advantage of impact printers is that multiple copies can usually be produced by using multipart paper interleaved with carbon, but their disadvantage is that they can be relatively noisy. Nonimpact printers on the other hand are usually very quiet but it is not usually possible to produce multiple copies. Printers can also be classified according to the sequence in which printing takes place. Some devices, like a typewriter, print one character at a time working left to right across a page. These are known as character printers or serial printers. The other type print randomly along the print line, gradually building up the complete line. These are known as line printers.

2.2.1 *Line printers*

Some impact printer devices follow the typewriter technique of having the character strike a ribbon which presses against the paper, so transferring the shape of the character to it. Other types use hammers; here a hammer behind the paper forces it to press against the ribbon, which in turn presses against the type, thus transferring the image.

Chain, train and belt printers use several complete sets of type which move horizontally past the print line, and are separated from the paper by an inked ribbon. In the case of the chain printer, the type characters literally form a chain, like links of a bicycle chain. The train printer is very similar except that the type characters are not permanently joined together but can be individually attached or removed to the train carrier. Hence the character set can be varied very easily. The belt printer has a series of slim metal uprights that are secured to a horizontal rotating belt, the type character being on the top of the upright. Depending on the particular printing mechanism, chain, train and belt printers may be character printers or line printers. The drum or barrel printer has complete character sets wrapped around the circumference of the barrel at every print position. If the printer is a 132-character width printer then there are 132 complete sets of type wrapped round the barrel. There are also 132 hammers, one for each print position, with the inked ribbon and print paper sandwiched between the hammers and the barrel. As the barrel revolves and brings a particular character in line with the paper in every print position, the hammer(s) corresponding to that position in which the character is required strikes the paper. Consequently in one complete revolution of the barrel, all the characters will have passed the paper, and the complete line will have been printed.

Speeds for all these types of printers and other printing devices are shown in Fig. 2.2.

2.2.2 *Dot matrix printer*

The dot matrix printer prints a pattern of dots in the shape of a character. The position of these dots is formed, for example, by a matrix of seven vertical dot positions and five horizontal dot positions.

	'Line' printers			'Character' printers		
	Speed	Charac-ter	Special paper	Speed	Charac-ter	Special paper
Chain/train/ belt	200– 2000 LPM	Full	No	30– 400 CPS	Full	No
Barrel	125– 3000 LPM	Full	No			
Dot matrix				30– 600 CPS	Dot	No
Daisy-wheel				30– 60 CPS	Full	No
Ink jet				100 CPS	Dot	No
Thermal				10– 30 CPS	Dot	Yes

Fig. 2.2

The print head contains seven wires that can strike an inked ribbon which is sandwiched between the print head and the paper. Each character is formed by the print head moving to each of the five horizontal dot positions and the appropriate wires striking the paper. Clearly because of the number of strikes per line required the speed is restricted.

2.2.3 *Daisy-wheel printers*

The print mechanism of the daisy-wheel printer consists of a flat disc with petal like projections. At the end of each projection is an embossed character which on impact with the paper will transfer the image of the character.

Advantages of the daisy-wheel printer are that there are few moving parts, printing can be performed in either direction, paper can be fed up or down, it has a low noise level, the type fount is easily changed and the print quality is high.

2.2.4 *Thermal printers*

Thermal printers have print heads that convert electricity to heat. The image is created on special heat-sensitive paper by the heated wires in the print head, in a similar way to that of the dot matrix printer. There is no inked ribbon required since the images are created by heat.

These printers are generally used where the volume of output is small because the heat-sensitive paper is relatively expensive. Speed is low because the heated wires of the print head must cool before moving to the next position.

2.2.5 Ink jet printers

These printers employ a technique which consists of spraying a stream of electrically charged ink droplets on to ordinary paper to produce printed characters. Character formation is performed by electrostatic deflection plates that control the direction of the charged ink droplets in much the same manner as the electron beam movement is controlled within a television set. Although reasonably fast for serial printers, their disadvantage is that they are relatively expensive.

2.2.6 Drum and flatbed plotters

Plotters are devices that output line drawings on paper. They consist of a pen which can either be touching the paper or lifted off it. It can be moved a short distance (e.g. 1 millimetre) either horizontally or vertically or, by moving both horizontally and vertically at the same time, generate a line at 45 degrees.

A line, curved or straight, is represented as a series of very short incremental lines, each one at the angle which most closely approximates the desired line. Because of this principle, curved or straight lines can be produced, so that the plotter is able to produce bar charts, line graphs, engineering drawings, maps and many other two- or even three-dimensional illustrations, all fully annotated. The paper is usually plain although it could be preprinted if necessary.

There are two types of plotter; the drum plotter and the flatbed plotter. On a drum plotter, in order to achieve the required movement of the pen relative to the paper, the pen moves across the paper left to right or right to left and the paper (one end of which is wrapped round a drum) rotates around the drum so that the paper and pen are moving relative to each other in an up and down direction.

On a flatbed plotter the paper is stationary and only the pen moves across and/or up and down the paper. The advantage of the flatbed plotter is that it can draw illustrations up to two metres square whereas the drum plotter is limited to drawings of only about one metre wide, although since the paper is on a continuous roll quite long drawings are possible.

2.2.7 Computer output microfilm (COM)

The adaptation of microfilm to the computer as an output medium was introduced a number of years ago and is still a valuable option in cases where large volumes of printed output have to be kept. Although microfilm media for data storage are available in several forms the most common is called microfiche. Microfiche is a small card of microfilm with many small images as a grid pattern. Usually the output from the computer is written to magnetic tape. A special machine reads the tape and transfers the data to microfiche. Subsequently microfiche can be inserted into a simple reader which enlarges the image and projects it on to a screen for the user to read. It can also be duplicated, and the multiple hard copies can be printed from it if required.

The following are some of the advantages and disadvantages of COM.

Advantages	*Disadvantages*
1 Speed of output is 10 to 20 times faster than high-speed line printers.	1 Requires special viewing equipment.
2 Very compact storage capability.	2 If printed copy is required a special reader/printer is needed.
3 Cost of developing microfilm is low compared to traditional paper costs.	
4 Distribution costs are low.	

Because of the above disadvantages microfilm is generally economical only when a high volume of documents is regularly output or where large files of printed data must be retained.

2.3 Input/output devices

There are a number of peripheral devices which to the user are a combined input and output device. There is some means whereby the user can input data or commands to the computer and there is also some means by which the computer can output information back to the user. These devices are particularly useful in situations which require a user to interact with the computer such as on a multiple terminal network system. It must be emphasized however, that as far as the computer is concerned these are entirely separate devices. One is an input device, the other an output device. The fact that they may share the same cabinet is of no consequence to the computer. Two very common devices will be considered.

2.3.1 *Visual display unit and keyboard*

The keyboard is essentially very similar to the keyboard of a card punch or paper tape punch except that depressing a key does not result in a character being punched, but in the character being transmitted directly to the computer. In most systems the character is also displayed on the visual display unit screen. Bearing in mind that the keyboard and display are two separate peripheral devices that share a common case, what actually happens is that when the computer receives the character from the input keyboard it sends this character back to the output display. This happens so quickly that the two operations appear simultaneous. This is known as echoing.

Visual display devices were developed as an alternative to printing devices for situations in which it is not essential to have a printed copy. Their chief advantages are that they are virtually silent, and can, if desired, display information at far greater speeds than any printing device.

The visual display unit is essentially like a small television screen and displays information in a very similar manner to that of a television set. In a simple form they are inexpensive but more expensive ones may offer special features. These include colour, flashing characters, variable intensity, protected areas on the screen, and the ability to go back to a prior point to delete or correct characters. If the device has a built in memory (which it must have to allow the correction of characters) it will allow the user to 'roll back' or redisplay lines that have 'rolled off' the top of the screen.

2.3.2 *Typewriter terminals*

These are very similar in principle to the visual display unit except that the output side of the device is a hard copy printer rather than a display screen. On this printer, which uses a moving, rotating or pivoting print head, the print device moves serially across the print line, the print head striking an ink ribbon which is between the print head and the paper.

2.4 Television technology

There have been a number of recent developments in the transmission of data which employ a domestic television set as the peripheral device. Two of the main developments are known as viewdata and teletext.

The term viewdata was introduced to describe a new information service being developed by the British Post Office in the early seventies. The information available through the service is stored on a computer system and is accessible to anyone who has a television and a telephone (and an adaptor). Since that time a number of other countries have either signed agreements with the British Telecom or begun to design their own systems. Consequently the term viewdata has become a name for the *type* of service, the British Telecom's system now being called PRESTEL.

Teletext is the general name given to such systems as those developed by the UK television companies. The BBC's version is known as CEEFAX and ITV's version is known as ORACLE. In a teletext system the data that can be transmitted to the user is also stored on a computer system. However, there is a very important difference between teletext and viewdata. In the case of viewdata the information is transmitted via the public telephone network whereas teletext information is transmitted with the television signals. One disadvantage of teletext is that to make the information available on demand, because it is transmitted with television signals it must be transmitted continuously. Consequently the volume of data that is available is limited.

On the other hand, since viewdata is accessed by the public telephone network, there is no theoretical restriction on the volume of information that can be accessed. There is of course a practical one, fixed by the size of the computer being used. More importantly, the user is allowed to enter data as well as use the data entry device to specify what information is required. When the system is fully developed, television sets will be available with adaptors and data entry devices built into them rather than as extras on an ordinary television set. These new sets will be capable of receiving both viewdata and teletext transmission.

Similar systems are being developed by television and telecommunication companies throughout the world, and readers are encouraged to investigate the facilities available in their own countries.

It may seem that the television set is being used merely as a convenient visual display unit to receive information transmitted from a computer. In many cases it will be, and this will provide access to an enormous amount of information, for the general public at their own convenience. However, one possible development is that of an 'intelligent' viewdata terminal. Such a device will be equipped with its own CPU and main memory, plus other peripherals such as a printer and perhaps floppy disk (see Chapter 3). This opens up the possibility of 'telesoftware'. With such a system, a program could be transmitted from the central computer system to the user's viewdata device and executed there. The advantage here is that the user does not have to pay for the connect time while the program is being executed but only during the transmission of the program into the viewdata terminal. This could be very useful in computer-aided learning (CAL) because each student can learn at his own pace and at the same cost. It could also be used to give access to business programs, and so provide a cheap form of small business computer service. One of the obvious problems, however, is how to prevent people from extracting programs from the system once and then keeping them indefinitely for their own use (a large part of the revenue for running viewdata is clearly from the connect time to it). When the system is fully available there will be a number of ways to overcome this.

2.5 Specific transducers

The advent of the microprocessor has highlighted the uses of computing machines for control of machine tools and other processes. This has entailed the development of devices which are able to measure some parameter of the product performance in a way which is readily converted to digital signals. A transducer is a device which is able to convert energy from one form to another. For example, a loudspeaker is a transducer which converts electronic signals to sound waves.

Most naturally occurring signals have an analogue nature; that is, they vary continuously. In order that such signals can be processed by a computer, they have to be converted into a digital form. This conversion is carried out by sampling the input signal at regular intervals and passing a value corresponding to the sampled value, to the computer. Such devices are called analogue-to-digital converters and will be a constituent part of any transducer sampling analogue signals. For example, a temperature sensor will require such a converter.

In the control of machine tools the digital output from the computer can be used directly to cause some on-off type action to be undertaken: for example, the starting of a drill. The subsequent lowering and raising of the drill would also be controlled digitally by, for example, having switches which are activated by the lateral movement of the drill.

Other transducers include magnetic switches and light activated switches, which can be interfaced directly with the circuitry of a computer. The advantage of such devices is their reliability and cost effectiveness. The main problem of contact switches is that they can cause switch bounce which gives more than one response when there should only be one.

The output from a computer cannot be used to drive directly a machine tool and there usually has to be some form of interface circuitry to allow the tool to be activated.

2.6 Summary

This chapter has indicated the large range of peripheral devices that are available and their areas of application. It is important that in any situation careful consideration is given as to the most appropriate peripheral device to employ. Not only does it have an effect on the speed of the task being performed but is often the basis by which 'users' judge the success or otherwise of a computer system, since it is their point of contact with the computing machine.

3 File store

In Chapter 1 the file store of a computing machine was introduced as a means of holding bulk information. The information which is held in a file store is either data or programs. This information is held in file store rather than main memory because main memory is relatively small in comparison to the file store and would soon become full. Most of the information held in a file store is only required for a short period when compared to the life of a computer and it is therefore more cost-effective to keep the information on the file store. A file store also has the advantage of being a permanent storage medium in that when power is switched off the information is still retained by the file store. This is not the case with most main memories where information is lost as soon as power is removed (see Chapter 4). A file store device can therefore be used as the storage medium upon which the permanent programs such as compilers and operating system, used by the computing machine are stored. The file store can be considered to be the second level in a storage hierarchy with main memory at the top level. Programs may only execute when the algorithm and the necessary data are in main memory. The computing machine therefore provides an efficient means of transferring information between file store and memory so that processing delays are reduced to a minimum. The remainder of this chapter discusses how file stores can be organized and the types of devices which can be used to provide file store systems.

3.1 Files records and items

The file store of a computer system is analogous to a filing system for stored paperwork which is held in a filing cabinet. Consider, for example, the file held by a general practitioner; the file comprises all the patients' records, each record containing the notes pertaining to a particular patient. Each record is differentiated by means of a unique identifier, usually the name and address of the patient. In the general practice environment there is only one such file, but in a hospital there will be many such files, each one associated with a different speciality within the hospital. Hence a hospital can be seen as a collection of files, a file being made up of similar records and the records each containing information about a patient.

The file store of a computer system is very similar in that it is split up into many named files each of which can be individually processed by just referring to the name given to the file. A file is a collection of similar records, that is within a file all records hold the same kind of information in the same structure. The structure of records can vary between files because different files hold different information to which different records structures are appropriate. A record is constructed from data values from which information can be found for the user processing the file. Data has no intrinsic meaning; data only becomes information when it is surrounded by other symbols. The number '30' has no meaning because it has no context, it only becomes information when surrounded by "°C' for example. Within a record it is only necessary to store the data, because within the record it will be known that a particular data item is used to represent temperatures. The "°C' only needs to be added when the data is presented to the user who needs the information that the temperature was 30°C.

A paper file is usually organized into some order, known to the user of the file, so that a particular record in the file can be found quickly. For example, patients' records could be stored alphabetically by surname and forenames. The surname and forenames are data items within the record which are used to order the file and as such are called 'key' data items. The person's marital status would probably not be a key data item but would be stored in the record. In such a paper file the organization of the file is usually held in the memory of the person using the file and the user also knows the most efficient way to access a piece of information in the file.

In a file store maintained by a computer system the files can be organized in many ways of which three different ways predominate. The choice of a particular organization depends upon the use to which the file is going to be put. These organizations are known as sequential, indexed-sequential and random.

3.1.1 *Sequential files*

A sequential file is one in which the records are stored and maintained in a predefined order specified by the user. Within such a file there is no means of adding records into the middle of the file except by copying, into another file, the records of the file up to the position of the new record, adding the new record and then copying the remainder of the original file. A similar process is needed to delete a record from the file, except that the record to be deleted is not copied to the new version of the file. In order to be able to manipulate a particular record, the file is processed from the beginning until the desired record is found. There is no direct analogy between a paper file and a sequential because the human operator usually has some idea of the location of records, so that he does not always have to search the file from the beginning.

3.1.2 *Indexed-sequential files*

An indexed-sequential file is one which is maintained in the same order as a sequential file except that usually some space is left for the addition of records. This organization is augmented by indexes which allow the search for a particular record to be started at some point within the file, thus reducing the time to search for a particular record in the file. An indexed-sequential file is split up into smaller sections, each of which is maintained in sequential order. An index maintains the range of records kept in each section. To access a record therefore involves searching the index to find in which section the record resides and then searching the indicated section for the desired record. In a large file a hierarchy of indexes may be maintained so as to reduce the search time through the indexes. An indexed-sequential file can be processed in two ways; namely, sequentially or randomly. When it is processed sequentially, the index is ignored and processing commences with the first record in the file and proceeds in order to the last record. When the file is processed randomly the indexes are used to shorten the search time. Such files are used a great deal because their usage reflects the requirements of every-day applications. For example, consider the current account system of a bank. When an account holder comes to the bank to withdraw some money he wants an immediate response from the teller and so the file is processed randomly. It is impossible to guarantee that processing for the file will be in account number order. However, when the file is being processed to generate a report of all overdrawn accounts this can be done sequentially.

3.1.3 *Random files*

A random file utilizes the fact that every record location within the file has a unique address. This address is usually an integer ranging from one to the number of records in the file. When a record is to be processed, the key value of the record is taken and processed by means of a hashing algorithm. The effect of the hashing algorithm is to map the range of key values on to the number of records which can be stored in the file.

The simplest mapping is $1:1$ but this implies that there will be a location in the file for every key value. Normally this is not the case as most key fields contain some redundancy and therefore an $n:1$ mapping is employed. Redundancy within a key means that not all numerical combinations are used, for example, in a bank account number; part of it may represent the type of account. The nett effect of such a mapping is that it is possible for the hashing algorithm to generate the same record address for records with different key values. Hence the algorithm has to be able to deal with this, which is a situation known as synonyms. There are two simple solutions; first, the record is placed in the next empty record location to be found as the file is read in order. Secondly, the record is placed in the record location, nearest to the desired location, which is not occupied. The second solution involves accessing record locations to the left and right of the desired location whereas the first only requires access to records to the right.

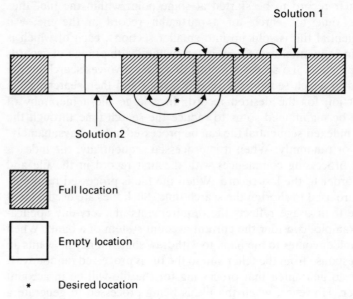

Fig. 3.1

3.1.4 *Filing systems and privacy*

A computer system is able to store and maintain many files for many different users and it is therefore vitally important that the different users are only able to gain access to those files to which they are entitled. Hence most computer systems use filing systems which enable users to maintain a record of the files which they own. In more flexible systems, users will be able to gain access to other users' files provided the owner of the file has granted the necessary access rights to the user wishing to gain access. Such systems usually involve the use of a password system.

When a file is created a user will have a set of access rights which he can associate with the file and by associating a password with a particular access right users who know the password will be able to gain access to the file. Typically the access rights could be: private, read only access, modify access, execute only. If a file is given the access right private then only the owner of the file will be allowed access to the file. Read only implies that users who know the password will be able to access the file but only for reading. Modify access implies that read and write access is allowed. Execute only means that the file contains a program which can only be executed by persons knowing the password. In a completely flexible system the owner of a file would be able to assign many different passwords to each of the access types in order to support the privacy requirements of complex filing systems.

3.2 Storage media

This section describes the techniques which can be used to implement the devices used to support file stores. It also shows how the different file organizations can be implemented on the devices. The majority of these devices use some form of magnetic recording facility. In simple terms, a magnetic field can be applied to a magnetic material causing the material to store the corresponding field. Thus it is possible to store binary information by recording fields of different density or by storing fields of different orientation. Information can be read from such a magnetic material by passing the material in front of a detector which is able to detect the magnetic field. The most common domestic use of magnetic recording techniques is that of a tape recorder. The main difference between the domestic and computing environments is that a computer records information in binary form whereas a tape recorder records analogue information. The analogue information requires a range of magnetic densities large enough to discriminate between the musical or speech frequencies.

3.2.1 *Tape storage*

Historically tape storage was the first magnetic storage device to be developed and it has been utilized by the computing industry in the following manner. A character of information is stored as a bit pattern in parallel across the width of the tape (see Fig. 3.2). The data is recorded together with a parity bit. A parity bit is a means of providing a check that the data has been stored correctly. If we consider an eight bit character of which one is the parity bit then either odd or even parity can be used. In even parity systems the number of bits set to '1' in the character code is summed and if the number is even the parity bit remains at '0' otherwise it is set to '1'. Hence it is possible to detect when there is an error in a character, but it is not possible to correct errors. The correction of errors is dealt with in Section 3.3.

Data is recorded on magnetic tape at the rate of either 800, 1600 or 6250 bits per inch which, because a character is stored across the tape, is also the rate at which characters are stored. The tape passes through the drive mechanism at 75 inches per second giving a data transfer rate of 60 to 470 kb/s (kb means kilobytes or thousand bytes). A magnetic tape is usually no longer than 2400 feet and can be as short as 100 feet. The amount of data

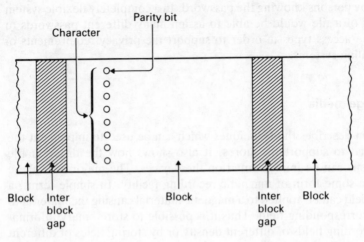

Fig. 3.2

which can be stored on one magnetic tape is therefore very large, ranging up to 180 Mb (Mb = mega-bytes or million bytes). It is therefore impossible to transfer the whole tape into the memory of a computer at one time. Hence the tape is logically split up into blocks and the tape mechanism transfers one block at a time. The tape therefore has to stop after the transfer of each block and has to be able to get up to full speed before it encounters the next block. The part of the tape used for stopping and starting is called the inter-block gap and it contains no information. The inter-block gap is usually of the order of $\frac{1}{2}$ to $\frac{3}{4}$ inch.

A block is used to store one or more records and the blocking factor of a particular file is the number of records stored per block. Some magnetic tape systems only have fixed length blocks, but the majority have variable length blocks because the user is best able to choose the size of the block commensurate with the application. There is a relatively simple tradeoff namely the larger the block the more data can be stored on the tape because of the fewer inter block gaps necessary but the larger the block the more memory is required to store the block.

If more than one record is stored per block, a block only has to be transferred to memory when all the records in the memory buffer have been processed. A memory buffer is the place to which a block is transferred. Hence every read issued from a program may not cause a transfer from the tape because there may still be records to be read in the buffer. This aspect of memory buffer management is usually transparent to the user, and the current state of the buffer is maintained by that part of the operating system controlling the magnetic tape subsystem.

Magnetic tape is usually only used to store sequential files because there is no means of moving the tape forwards and backwards at a sufficient speed to be able to carry out the random processing required by the other file organizations.

Magnetic tape drives can take several forms. The most usual on mainframe computers is the reel to reel system using $\frac{1}{2}$ inch wide tape. The tape is passed from one reel to another and when processing is complete the tape has to be rewound on to the original reel. Several mini- and microcomputers use a cassette mechanism which is very similar to an audio cassette and uses $\frac{1}{4}$ inch wide tape. These cassette mechanisms tend to be very much slower, as data is stored serially rather than in parallel but the tape and drives are very much cheaper. There is also a cartridge system which employs $\frac{1}{2}$ inch wide tape and uses the same technique as the reel to reel, except that the tape is totally enclosed in the cartridge.

A mass storage device has been developed that accommodates many hundreds of cartridges which can be automatically loaded into the drive mechanism. This device has a storage capacity measured in thousands of millions of bytes but access to a particular byte is relatively rapid because the storage capacity is physically split up into the cartridges which can be loaded fairly quickly (10 to 15 seconds).

3.2.2 *Disk storage*

A disk storage system comprises two major parts, of which the first is a circular plate, mounted on a central spindle. The plate is coated with a magnetic material, usually on both sides of the plate. The diameter of the plate can vary from 5 to 15 inches depending upon the disk system. Secondly there is a read/write head assembly which is able to move across the surface of the plate while the plate is made to rotate. In smaller disk systems there will only be one such complete assembly; however, in larger systems many plates will be stacked upon the same spindle, each surface having its associated read/write head assembly. The structure of a multi-plate disk is shown in Fig. 3.3, in such a system all the read/write heads are attached to a common movement so that all heads are in the same position relative to the disk surface.

In order that the process of data transfer to and from the disk system can be understood it is first necessary to define some terms commonly associated with disk systems. A track is that part of the disk surface which can be read by one read/write head without moving the heads. On one surface the individual tracks make a series of concentric circles corresponding to the position of the head. The number of tracks per surface varies with systems but can be as few as 30 to as many as 400. In a multi-surface system a cylinder comprises all the tracks which can be read without moving the read/write heads. The system shown in Fig. 3.3 has 8 tracks per cylinder. The quantity of data which is stored in a track is usually too large to be transferred in one read to the computer system's memory. A track is

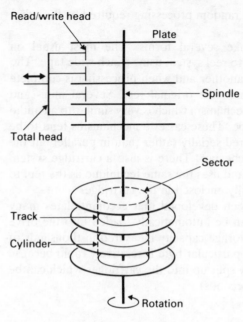

Fig. 3.3 Disk structure

therefore subdivided into a number of sectors, a sector being the unit of data transfer between the disk and the memory. A sector may contain several, one or part of a record depending upon the application. The disk system has a means of determining the current position of the disk relative to the read/write heads so that it can process the correct sector. Between each sector there is an intersector gap, which contains addressing information and provides sufficient time for the disk electronics to switch between one track and another within the same cylinder. The intersector gap does not provide sufficient time for the head to be moved between one cylinder and another and also be able to read 'consecutive' sectors.

Every access to the disk could involve a head movement plus a time to wait for the appropriate sector to come under the read/write heads. There is usually a larger time penalty if many cylinders have to be traversed and it is therefore normal for files to be allocated to contiguous cylinders. To overcome some of the delays, disk systems are being constructed which have more than one read/write assembly. It is then possible to read and write from each assembly at the same time in such a system.

In order that data can be accessed from the disk it is necessary for the software to provide the cylinder, track and sector values of the data to be processed. The disk system then moves the heads accordingly, and the data can subsequently be transferred. Most disk systems usually incorporate a 'retry' mechanism, as a means of ensuring data accuracy. That is, when data is written to the disk it is immediately read back, after waiting one rotation, to ensure that the stored data is the same as that transmitted to the disk system. If it is not the same, several attempts are made to write the data on the disk. If none of these is successful, a disk error has occurred which will require maintenance to be carried out upon the system to ascertain the reason for the fault. Most systems do not employ a retry mechanism upon reading data because this process is not prone to errors.

Before a disk can be used, it has to be formatted; this usually means storing the cylinder track and sector numbers in the intersector gap prior to each sector on the disk. This information is read at the same time as the following sector is processed, and thus provides an added check that the correct sector is being processed. That is, the sector address provided by the software matches that provided from the disk. If there was no match, it would usually imply that the disk hardware was not functioning correctly.

Disk systems take many forms which are commonly categorized as floppy, hard and fixed or exchangeable. Floppy and hard relate to the nature of the base material upon which the magnetic material is coated. If it is constructed from flexible plastic material the term floppy is used. If the material is rigid the term hard is used. Floppy systems tend to be much cheaper, not be so critical in their manufacturing tolerances but also have a much slower data transfer rate and smaller data capacity than hard disc systems. Floppy disks tend to predominate in microcomputer systems where the requirement for large fast disk storage is not necessary.

A fixed disk system is one in which it is not possible to remove the disk(s) from the drive mechanism. An exchangeable disk system is one in which the disk can be removed and replaced by a different disk. An exchangeable system allows for unlimited storage but only a part of the total can be accessed at any one time.

3.2.3 *Bubble memories*

A bubble memory is a magnetic device in which magnetic 'bubbles' can be manipulated in such a way as to store data. The devices comprise a base plate upon which a pattern of electrical plates is arranged. An alternating current can be applied to each of the plates in turn so as to cause the movement of magnetic material from one plate to the next. Upon the base plate a magnetic fluid is placed and kept in contact with the base plate by being encapsulated. The complete assembly is then held in a magnetic field which ensures that the fluid particles are all aligned in the same direction. Within the assembly there is a means of causing a particle of the fluid to be magnetically reversed, thus forming a bubble of reverse magnetization to the majority of the fluid. There is also a mechanism by which it is possible to detect the magnetization of a particular bubble. The structure is shown in Fig. 3.4.

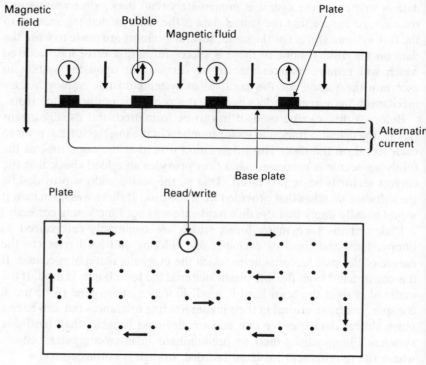

Fig. 3.4 Structure of bubble memory

The operation of the bubble memory is as follows. Data is written to the memory by sending the bit pattern to the memory, whenever there is a one bit the write assembly causes the current bubble to be inverted relative to the rest of the fluid. If there is a zero then the bubble has the same orientation as the rest of the fluid. The applied alternating current then causes the bubble to move to the next plate and so on until the whole of the data has been encoded. The choice of field and size of alternating current are critical so as to ensure that the bubble does not change its state. Data is read by passing the stream of data bits past the read point. Hence the memory has to wait until the required data passes the read point. In larger memories data is organized into smaller blocks as shown in Fig. 3.5. When data from a particular block is required it is shifted into the outer path and then back into the block.

Such devices, although cheap and small are relatively slow, and tend to be used in applications where speed is not essential. Such an example is a portable terminal in which it is possible to store data, then connect the terminal to an acoustic coupler and thus to a computer. The stored data can now be transferred from the memory. These devices are also not

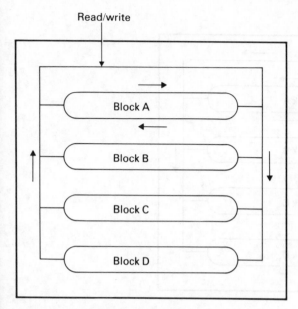

Fig. 3.5 Large bubble memory organization

volatile, which means that in such applications standard information can be maintained by the terminal at all times.

3.2.4 *Charge coupled devices*

A charge coupled device is very similar to a bubble memory except that electric charges are transferred rather than magnetic bubbles and that the whole device can be constructed by means of semiconductor techniques. The only further requirement is that because an electrical charge leaks away the electrical state of each charge has to be periodically renewed. The structure of a charge coupled device is shown in Fig. 3.6.

Data is applied at the read/write point and a charge is either created or not depending upon the state of the current bit. The charge is then made to move by applying an alternating current to plates within the semiconductor material in the same way as the bubble memory. The data is then moved into one of the blocks in which it continually rotates through the amplifier thus ensuring that data is not lost. Data is read by passing charges from the appropriate block round the outer loop past the read point. The chief disadvantage of this memory is that when electrical power is removed data is lost, that is the device is volatile. Charge coupled memories are cheaper and faster than bubble memories and have a larger data capacity. In both cases, however, it is unlikely that they will be used as main memory in computer systems due to the delay in accessing the data. However, they

Read/write

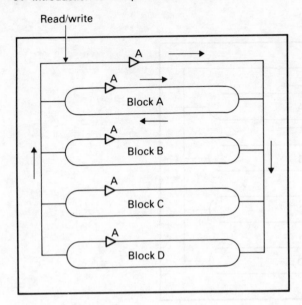

 Amplifier

Fig. 3.6 Structure of a charge-coupled device

are quite likely to be used as a more reliable form of mass storage possibly replacing the disk and tape systems. The cost differential is such that the replacement of disk systems is still a long time away.

3.2.5 *Content addressable file store*

Most data processing applications require records to be fetched from disk or tape storage and then processed to find out their current state; modifications are then made to only a few of the records, depending upon certain conditions and the records are then written back. In such an application every record is read into main memory, interrogated and in a large number of cases immediately written back to the storage device. A content addressable file store is essentially a disk system to which has been added some processing capability. The system is designed so that only those records to be processed are transferred to the main memory; those requiring no attention are never transferred. In such a system holding many different types of data it is necessary for the programmer to be able to specify details about the records and the condition(s) under which records are to be passed to the main memory. Once the content addressable file store has been so 'programmed' it will access all the records in the file and select only those which satisfy the conditions. Programming such a system requires a mechanism that can identify the fields and sizes of a record together with field values of the records desired for processing. This type of device therefore reduces the amount of work which has to be undertaken by the central processing unit and allows the CPU to do other work, thus increasing the efficiency of the overall system. Other techniques for improving system efficiency are described in Chapter 10.

3.3 Error checking

During the transfer of data from a disk or tape system to main memory data may become corrupted. It is therefore necessary to have some means of detecting errors which have occurred and possibly correcting them. These techniques can also be applied to the transmission of data in a communications link.

The first technique is to apply an augmented type of parity checking which thus ensures that the individual characters are correct. Other techniques generate a checksum mechanism to a block of data and so provide a check on the whole data.

The simple parity system described earlier is only able to detect an error but not correct it, and it is possible for more than one error in a character to be missed by the parity checking system. A simple expansion of the system is to have more parity bits which check only part of the character. Consider a four bit code in which the bits are named a, b, c, d and which has two parity bits P1 and P2. Parity P1 operates on bits a, b, c and parity bit P2 operates upon bits b, c, d. If P1 shows an error state then the error is known to be in bits a, b, c and similarly for parity bit P2 with b, c, d. If both parity bits are incorrect then it is known that bits b and c contain the error. By adding a third parity bit as follows it is possible to detect all errors and correct some of them:

P1   a b c
P2   b c d
P3   c d a

If P1 and P2 are in error, the implication is that bit b is in error and can therefore be corrected. In this example it can be seen that errors in bit c can be detected but not corrected.

Thus by adding more parity bits more checks can be undertaken, but the number of parity bits increases and thereby increases the possibility of error in the parity bits. The advantage of these parity systems is that when data correction can be undertaken it saves data transmission time because erroneous data does not need to be retransmitted.

The above system would, however, become extremely inefficient if in parallel transmission one of the transmission lines were to go down. Such errors are detected by the checksum mechanism. A checksum can be formed by adding together all the words to be transmitted, ignoring overflow. The resultant sum is called the checksum. The checksum is then transmitted after the data. On receipt of data the checksum is recalculated and checked with the transmitted checksum. If there is a discrepancy it is known that an error has occurred.

By combining these two techniques it is possible to detect errors at the character and the block level, and thereby provide a means of ensuring that stored data and transmitted data correspond.

3.4 Summary

This chapter has described methods by which bulk data storage of data can be achieved. The organization of the data so that it is held in a form useful to the programmer has also been considered in relation to the physical characteristics of the devices. Finally the concept of error checking has been introduced, and techniques have been briefly described that allow errors to be detected and in some cases corrected.

3.5 Problems

3.1 Choose a suitable file organization for the following applications and justify your answer. How would you organize the individual records of each file?
(1) current accounts for a bank
(2) hospital outpatients clinic records
(3) an appointments system for a small firm
(4) a payroll system
(5) a students' record system
(6) a library's catalogues and indexes

3.2 From current manufacturers' information find out the cost per byte of storage of the following storage media:
(1) hard disk
(2) floppy disk
(3) bubble memory
(4) charged coupled devices
(5) tape
From the same source of information find out
(a) the dimensions of the storage media and associated hardware
(b) the transfer rate

(c) the delay between data being requested and the data becoming available for transfer

(d) total storage capacity

NB: These figures will vary with manufacturer and type of media.

3.3 A magnetic tape of total length 2400 feet has data recorded on it at 1600 bits/inch. It utilizes an inter-block gap of $\frac{1}{2}$ inch. A file is stored upon the tape which contains records of 400 characters. What is the total capacity of the tape when the number of records per block is 1, 2, 3, 8, 10 or 16? How does this affect the size of memory buffer required?

4 Memory

Chapter 1 introduced the concept of a memory that could remember information which could be used subsequently by the computing machine. This information was identified as being of two types: first, sequences of instructions corresponding to an algorithm, and secondly data upon which the algorithm was to operate.

In order that an algorithm can be processed it is necessary for both the data and the instructions to be in the memory of the computer. In this chapter we shall expand this basic concept to show how different concepts in memory design and technology can be used to generate different memory structures. Each of the basic structures will be associated with a particular design criterion for which the computer architect has a design aim. In particular, the architect will choose a memory structure which satisfies the needs of a particular environment in the most cost-effective way. The memory technologies currently available follow the simple rule that the faster access there is to the memory the more expensive the memory. Hence any computer system will be constructed from a hierarchy of different memory technologies reflecting the most cost-effective balance for a particular computing environment.

4.1 The basic building blocks

Any memory is constructed from a collection of memory cells, each having its own unique name, commonly called an address. It is normal for these addresses to be assigned from the positive integers. Each of the memory cells contains a piece of data which is referred to as the contents of the cell. Another synonymous way of describing this data is as the contents of a memory location. Each memory cell or location usually holds one piece of data.

Figure 4.1 shows the normal structure of a unit of memory which is constructed from a number of cells.

Each collection of memory cells has associated with it two registers in the CPU known as the memory address register (MAR) and the memory buffer register (MBR). Registers will be discussed in detail in Section 4.2. A memory may be constructed from more than one such unit, in which

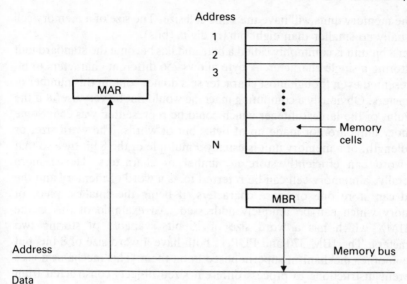

Fig. 4.1

case the MAR and MBR will be placed on a memory bus linking all the units together (see Chapters 6 and 8 for a description of the use of buses). The mode of operation of a memory unit is that the address of the particular cell to be processed is placed in the MAR. This address is decoded by some electronics which then activate the correct memory cell in order that it may be processed. Because any of the cells can be processed at random, this type of memory is called random access memory (RAM). A memory cell can be processed in one of two ways: first, it can be read; that is, the contents of the memory cell are placed in the MBR from where other parts of the CPU may process the data (see Section 6.1.2). Secondly the memory cell may be written into. This is carried out by a data value being placed in the MBR by some means external to the memory, and then being copied into the addressed memory location. During a read the contents of a memory cell remain unaltered; that is, the data is not destroyed. During a write the contents of a memory cell are replaced by the value in the MBR, and any data which may have been previously stored in the cell is thus destroyed. The memory cells themselves are therefore separated from the rest of the CPU by means of the two registers MAR and MBR. All communication between the CPU and memory is via these two registers.

The size of a memory cell varies from computer to computer. More precisely, if we interpret the contents of a memory cell as an integer, the modulus of the maximum value varies between memory units. If a computer system has more than one memory unit then, as a general rule, all the memory units will have the same cell size. The size of a memory cell is usually no smaller than eight binary digits (bits).

An 8 bit unit is commonly called a byte and has become the standard unit for storing a single character. A byte allows 256 different characters to be represented even though most character sets do not contain this number of characters. Obviously a computing machine would not be very useful if the modulus of the largest integer which could be represented was 255. Some memory units are not made up of bytes but of words. The word size, or wordlength, of a memory unit is usually a multiple of the 8 bit byte so that the word can efficiently store a number of characters. Hence more generally, a memory cell can be referred to as a word of memory and the word can store one or more characters, it being the smallest piece of memory which can be uniquely addressed. An example of this is the HP21MX which has a word size of 16 bits, capable of storing two characters. The IBM 370 and PDP-11 both have a word size of 8 bits but have another mechanism superimposed upon them. This mechanism uses different instructions to process different sized objects constructed from several bytes (see Chapter 5). The PDP-11 has instructions capable of processing two and four bytes, referred to as words and double-words. On the IBM 370, bytes can be combined into two, four and eight byte units. These are referred to as half-words, full-words and double-words respectively. However, on both the IBM 370 and PDP-11 the basic memory unit is the byte, even though other mechanisms are used to enable numbers of sufficiently large value to be manipulated.

It is in the decisions about word size and the way memory is to be manipulated by instructions that we can first see the role of the architect in memory design. If it is known that the machine is going to be designed for a data processing environment in which a lot of character information will be processed, the architect may opt for a byte oriented memory. However, in numerical and process control environments it is more likely that a much larger word size will be used, e.g. 60 bits. The disadvantage of a large word size is that when storing characters space may be wasted or extra processing may be required. The disadvantage of byte or character oriented memories is that, in order to retrieve a number, several accesses to the memory will be required, unless there are some extra electronics associated with memory to allow sequences of bytes to be accessed. Obviously this extra facility increases the cost of the memory unit, and has to be considered when these decisions are taken.

4.2 Dedicated registers

Not all the memory in a computing machine will be accessed via the MBR and MAR. In order that the computing machine can function efficiently there may have to be registers which are special storage locations that are not part of main memory and consequently can be accessed without recourse to the MAR and MBR. Such registers are usually few, and have a fixed use within the overall structure and operation of the computing machine. The use to which these registers is put is discussed more fully in Section 6.1.1 and by implication in Chapter 5. During the processing of an instruction, data may have to be temporarily stored. For example, when adding two integers together the integers could be stored in two registers and the result in a third before it is transferred to some other location within the computer system. If these registers were in main memory, the above process would be impossible, because we can only access one location of memory at a time, with the memory structure so far discussed. Perhaps more important is the fact that accessing a register is much quicker, because no addressing mechanism is needed (see Chapter 5), the register being accessed directly as required by an instruction.

The registers which have been discussed so far are somewhat special in that, normally, the user of the computing machine is unaware of their existence. Further, these registers are designed to do a specific job and are not bound by the word size of the computer. There is no point in having an 8 bit register if a 2 bit one will do. There are within a computing machine many one bit registers which are known as flags or *flip-flops*. These registers are able to store the state of some part of the CPU and can be tested by other parts of the CPU.

It is also common for a computing machine to have one or more registers which are available for use by the user by means of his programs. Such registers, for example, can be used to hold intermediate data values when evaluating expressions. Hence the user's program will execute more quickly because these registers are directly accessible by a unique name, inherent within the instruction. If there were no registers, all intermediate data values would have to be stored in the memory via the MBR and MAR, which is a very much slower process.

The role of the architect can be seen here again. By making a number of registers available to the user, the cost of the computing machine will be increased, but the ease and flexibility of use will be much greater than that of a computer which has fewer registers. The greater the set of instructions that are available to a computing machine, then probably the more internal registers will be used; the cost will rise but the computer will be more generally versatile.

4.3 Von Neumann memory organization

John Von Neumann was one of the first people to put forward a mathematical theory that could be applied to the construction of a computing machine. A large part of this theory was concerned with the development of a memory which could be used to store the instructions and data of a program, the so-called stored program concept. Fundamental to this theory was the idea of a linear array of memory cells that could be used to store both the instructions of the algorithm and the data. This was a big step forward from early calculating machines in which the algorithm was remembered, or stored, by the operator. Unfortunately the design of the theory was somewhat deficient. Two important difficulties were that only one location of memory could be accessed at one time and that there was no physical separation between instructions and data.

As has been seen, in the case of the addition of two numbers, the computing machine needs access to two or three registers concurrently. Thus the restriction on access to the memory necessitated the use of registers which are probably not strictly necessary. Another effect of having an addressed linear array is that the address of every required memory location has to be known. It is easier to conceive of data records in which the remainder of the record can be processed when the value of part of the record is known. Finally, because there was no distinction between data and instructions, disastrous consequences could result from trying to obey or use data as instructions. Disasters should not occur when a program works correctly, but they may when programs are being tested. For example, a data value obeyed as an instruction may cause branching to an area of memory that is not supposed to be accessed by this program.

Up to the mid 1970s all commercially available computing machines had a memory structure similar to that propounded by Von Neumann. It is only since then that machines have become available which have attempted to remove the straight jacket imposed by the Von Neumann architecture. The remainder of this chapter discusses these techniques, many of which were developed before the mid 1970s but are only now being applied in situations unrelated to the Von Neumann architecture. The reason is that semiconductor technology has made it possible to mass produce the required memory structures. The final section of this chapter will deal with the technological developments.

4.4 Associative memories

An associative memory, or content addressable memory is one which does not require the use of a MAR and MBR because data is accessed via the content of the registers used in the memory. Figure 4.2 shows the structure of a simple associative memory.

The associative and conventional fields comprise a memory location such that if the associative field is changed the conventional field has to be changed as well. These memory locations are filled with data. Subsequent-

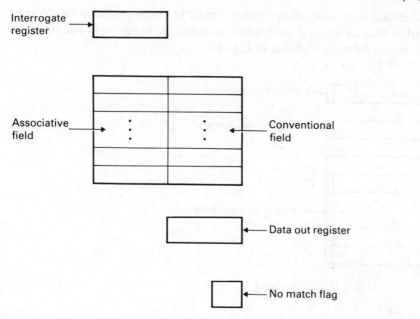

Interrogate
register

Associative
field

Conventional
field

Data out register

No match flag

Fig. 4.2

ly a data value is placed in the interrogate register. This value is then compared in parallel with (that is, at the same time as) the contents of the associative field of all memory locations. If one of the associative fields contains the same value as the interrogate register then the value in the corresponding conventional field is placed in the data out register for subsequent processing by the CPU. If none of the associative fields contains the required data value then a no-match condition is set in a flag associated with the associative memory. Thus this mechanism allows the processing of many memory locations in parallel based not on the address of the location but upon its content. Because processing is carried out in parallel, it is much quicker than using a linear array of addressable memory locations. In this form the associative memory is somewhat limited in that it cannot deal with multiple matches as it has only one data out register. This deficiency could be overcome if there was a processor which was associated with each memory location in the associative process. Such systems are becoming more feasible with the development of cheap memories and processing units.

An associative memory using a single data out register was used in this form in the early 1960s in a computer called ATLAS which used the memory to control an addressing mechanism called paging. The user program had no control over the associative memory. Paging is described in Section 4.8. Developments were undertaken to the simple system described here so that the facility could be made available to the user rather than an internal mechanism not available to the user. The structure of such a memory is shown in Fig. 4.3.

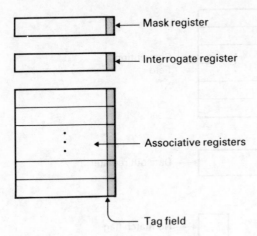

Fig. 4.3

Its operation proceeds as follows. The associative registers are filled with data values and prior to a set of interrogations the associated tag fields, which are one bit long, are reset to zero. The interrogate register is filled with a data value such that the fields of the data correspond in position to the fields within the data stored in the associative registers, i.e., multi-field data can be processed. The mask register has bits set and cleared so that only those bits that are set in the mask will cause the corresponding bits to be compared in the subsequent associative processing. For example, if bits 8, 9, 10 are set to 1 in the mask register the other bits being cleared to zero, then only bits 8, 9, 10 in the associative registers will be compared with the interrogate register. This means that only selected fields within the data can be used. Those memory locations for which there is match between the interrogate register and the associative registers will have their tag field set to one. The interrogate and mask registers can now be changed and, by including the tag field, further passes through the associative memory can be undertaken which will produce logical combinations from the data values stored in the memory locations. When the desired sequence of interrogations has been undertaken all locations in the associative register which have a tag field of either one or zero, whichever is appropriate to the solution, can be processed. If only one processing unit is available, the data will have to be processed serially; otherwise it can be processed in parallel. Even if there is only one processing unit, there will be a speed advantage over a normal memory, because the processing unit has only to test the state of the one bit tag field rather than the multifield record. As an example of the sort of processing which can be undertaken by such a unit, consider the following. The data comprises three fields and it is desired to find those memory locations for which the following logical condition holds:

not ((field 1 = 2 or field 2 = 3) and field 3 = 4).

Assuming the associative registers have been filled and the tag fields are reset to zero, and remembering that the tag field is set to one after an interrogation which finds a match in a particular location, the sequence of operations required would be:

- Set field 1 of interrogate to 2
- Set mask so that field 1 is considered, interrogate
- Set field 2 of interrogate to 3
- Set mask so that field 2 is considered, interrogate
- Set tag field of interrogate to 1
- Set tag field of mask to 1
- Set field 3 of interrogate to 4
- Set mask so that field 3 is considered, interrogate
- Process those records with tag field of zero.

A simple extension which can be added to the above scheme is to incorporate a mechanism which allows the relation to be varied from equality to include the usual arithmetic relational operators ($< \leqslant = \neq \geqslant >$).

One of the major drawbacks of such associative memories is their limited size, in that the size of each associated register is fixed as is the number of associative registers in the memory. A simplification of the above mechanism is used in Prime 750 computers.

4.5 Cache memories

A cache memory introduces the concept of memory hierarchy. A hierarchical memory is one which is constructed from different types of memory. The type of memory is usually differentiated by the speed at which the memory is able to process data. Hence a three level memory could be constructed from high, medium and slow speed memories. The reasons for introducing memory hierarchies are many and will be discussed in more detail in Section 4.8. The cache memory was introduced to solve a specific problem in computer architecture and was the first attempt at using memories of different speeds. The problem which had to be overcome was speeding up the execution of instructions. An analysis of programs revealed that the majority of programs used only a very few memory locations for the storage of variables (excluding arrays). Thus if these variables could be collected together in a special memory which was of higher speed the execution speed of the program could be increased. Such a memory is called a cache memory.

A cache memory holds the variables of the currently executing program. Obviously these variables have to be loaded from the main memory, where the instruction sequence is stored, before the program is executed. The size of the cache memory has to be chosen so that most programs will be able to fit their variables into the cache. The instruction set (see Chapter 5) will have to be augmented to take account of the situation where there is insufficient room in the cache. In this case, some of the variables will have to be held in main memory. A more sophisticated cache memory would have a facility for ensuring that the most frequently accessed variables would be held in the cache. This would be done by keeping a count of the number of accesses made to a particular variable. By sampling these counts at regular intervals the most frequently accessed variables can be moved to the cache. This technique is used on computers designed in the late 1970s onwards, such as Harris S800, Prime 750, IBM 4341 and ICL 2900 computers.

4.6 Interleaved and segmented memories

An interleaved memory was first used on a CDC 6600 computer as a means of speeding up access to the memory. In the mid 1960s, memory access speed was, and even now is, a critical factor, which was slowing down the overall execution speed of a computing machine. An interleaved memory is one in which the memory is split up into banks, each with its own memory address and buffer registers. Each bank is constructed from the same type of memory. Thus it is possible to access as many words of memory as there are banks in the interleaved memory.

Obviously such a system requires more complex control of the generation of addresses. When a piece of data is to be fetched from the memory the address of the data item is generated within the CPU. In an interleaved memory, part of the address is used to indicate which memory bank is to be used. Before the address can be sent to the bank's MAR it must be ascertained whether the bank is already busy. If the bank is not busy then the address can be sent immediately to the bank. When the bank is busy the address cannot be sent and therefore it has to be retained within the memory control system. Obviously this could occur for more than one of the banks and the following solution can be adopted as shown in Fig. 4.4. Registers R1 to R4 form a queue through which an address passes if it cannot be accepted by its memory bank. R0 is the register into which addresses are placed on entry to the mechanism. If the required bank is

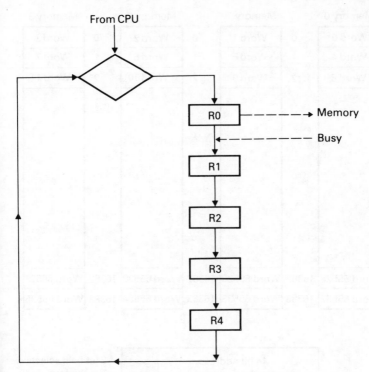

Fig. 4.4

busy, a signal is returned to the control system, and the address passes into R1. If the required bank is free, the address passes to the appropriate memory bank. The priority mechanism ensures that if there is an address in R4 it is passed to R0 rather than allowing a new address into the mechanism from the CPU; in this way the address in R4 has another chance of being accepted. Obviously it is now possible for the sequence in which operands are fetched from memory to be altered, because a bank was busy and the bank for the next address in sequence was not. Hence addresses and operands from memory are given a tag which allows them to be processed in the correct order.

A program is a sequence of instructions, and therefore the best way of using an interleaved memory is to place the instructions in separate banks so that there is never any contention, except when data is being fetched. This can be achieved by making the bits of the address which indicate the bank, the least significant part of the address as illustrated in Fig. 4.5. To reduce further the contention for banks of memory, it may be possible to store data in some of the banks and instructions in the remainder of the banks.

Address	Memory 0		Memory 1		Memory 2		Memory 3
0	Word 0	0	Word 1	0	Word 2	0	Word 3
1	Word 4	1	Word 5	1	Word 6	1	Word 7
2	Word 8	2	Word 9	2	Word 10	2	Word 11
	• • •		• • •		• • •		• • •
16382	Word 65528	16382	Word 65529	16382	Word 65530	16382	Word 65531
16383	Word 65532	16383	Word 65533	16383	Word 65534	16383	Word 65535

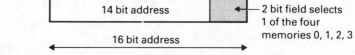

14 bit address — 2 bit field selects 1 of the four memories 0, 1, 2, 3

16 bit address

Note that the MAR of each memory only needs to be 14 bits wide

Fig. 4.5

4.6.1 *Segmented memories*

A segmented memory is very similar to an interleaved memory, except that it is not usual to distribute a sequence of instructions amongst several of the banks. Each of the banks of a segmented memory has its own memory address and buffer registers, and the CPU contains some control logic which ensures that addresses are not sent to a segment until that segment is idle. This control logic is not as complex as that for an interleaved memory because each segment only holds information of a single type. It is usual to have data and instruction segments, and the data segments may be further subdivided by use. For example, the Zilog Z8000 processor chip includes a segmented memory in which segments are used for the operating system, programmer instructions, programmer data and a stack. The use of each segment is defined by the programmer himself. Because the segment has a singular use the contention problem is reduced, because the memory is alternately accessing an instruction segment and a data segment. (See Chapter 6 for further details of instruction processing.)

Another use to which a segmented memory can be put is that of context switching. In a computer system which is capable of supporting more than one user concurrently, it is necessary to switch from one user's program to another. In a simple linear memory this may mean that the memory holds each program in a different area of memory. If the memory is not sufficiently large, the programs may have to be swapped into memory from file store. A more elegant and intrinsically safer solution is to put each program into a separate segment of memory. When it is the turn of a particular program to be allowed to process, all that is switched is the segment that is being addressed. Obviously there can only be as many concurrent users as there are memory segments. The system is much safer than a linear memory, because there is no way in which a program can overwrite part of another program. The two are in different segments of the memory and the segment information is appended to the address by the CPU and not by the user.

4.7 Tagged memories

This is a technique for labelling the contents of a memory location to indicate the type of data stored in the location. The label is called a tag. A tagged memory is a useful concept, because it can be used to ensure that data in the memory is protected from misuse.

The simplest type of tagged memory will differentiate between instructions and data, and so ensure that instructions are not accessed as data and vice versa. This simple mechanism can be extended in many different ways. The type of the data can be differentiated so that instructions designed to operate upon characters, fixed-point numbers and floating-point numbers only operate upon data of the required type. Some computing machines use variable length instructions, and a tagged memory can be used to indicate the length of an instruction. The Burroughs B5000 computers used a system similar to the technique described above.

4.8 Paged memories

One of the most important aspects of current memory technology (see 4.10) is that memory is becoming cheaper to produce in large quantities, but that there is still a significant price differential between high speed and low speed memories. The fact that memory has become cheaper can be seen from the development of computer systems through the 1970s. At the outset of the decade, a 1 megabyte machine was a large machine, but by the end of the decade microprocessors were being developed which could sensibly use 48 megabytes of memory (mega = million).

With the availability of such large memories it became feasible to have memory hierarchies in which bulk storage was provided by large slow memories, while the data and instructions for the program being executed were moved to a higher speed smaller memory.

A program is divided into fixed length pages. When the program is initiated, these pages may be on file store or in the bulk memory. At this stage, the first page will be copied into the fast memory and execution will begin. In due course, a reference will be made to a page which is not in fast memory. This page is fetched and placed in the high speed memory and execution will proceed. In due course, the high speed memory will become full, and a page will have to be removed to the bulk memory. Obviously such a mechanism has to be controlled by the CPU. Some of the properties of the control mechanism are:

(a) the pages of a program in high speed memory do not have to be contiguous;

(b) a record of pages belonging to different programs must be maintained;

(c) a record of the most frequently accessed pages should be maintained;

(d) a record is kept of whether the page is data or instructions;

(e) a record of where pages are stored in bulk memory.

Property (a) is required so that pages do not have to be shuffled to maintain sequential order. They will probably not be required in sequential order in any case. Obviously addresses of memory locations within a program will relate to the start of the program and so there will have to be some means of translating a relative address into an address within the high speed memory. Relative addresses are normally stored as a page number and a word within a page. Hence all that is required is a mechanism which allows the CPU to find out where a particular page is stored in high speed memory and the word part of the relative address will give the offset from that location. The associative memory described in Section 4.4 will carry out this function.

When a program terminates, some of its pages will remain in high speed memory and will only be removed when pages for the next program require space. Thus pages from more than one program may be in the memory at the same time. Hence the necessity for property (b). This is further utilized when the following case is considered. A program is executing and then needs access to a page not in the high speed memory. Before the program can continue, this page has to be loaded into high speed memory. During this transfer time the CPU is idle; therefore another program can be given access to the CPU and can be allowed to execute. Thus within the same CPU it is possible to have more than one program in a state of execution but only one of the programs can be being executed at any particular time.

Property (c) is required so that when a page has to be removed from the high speed memory because another page is needed, a page which has not been accessed for a long time can be chosen. This is also decided in conjunction with property (d). Pages which contain program instructions do not have to be written back to bulk memory because they will never be altered. However, pages which contain data will have to be written back, because data values may have been changed. A variation of this technique is to keep a record of those pages which have been written to. The page most likely to be removed then is one which has not been accessed for a long time and which also has not been written to. The process which decides which page to remove is called the page turning algorithm. When a page is to be transferred from bulk memory to high speed memory and vice versa the location of the page in bulk memory has to be known, giving rise to the necessity for property (e).

The technique of paging has been described between two hierarchical memories but in fact it can be extended easily to a hierarchy of many memories. Further, paging gives rise to a concept known as virtual memory. The memory from which programs can be executed is necessarily much smaller than the bulk memory. It is possible in fact to construct programs which require far more space than is available to the high speed memory. The page mechanism ensures that only the pages currently required reside in high speed memory. We can consider the high speed memory to be the real (i.e. existing) memory in which the program can execute, and the program to exist in a virtual memory supported by bulk memory and file store. In fact some computing machines (ICL 2900) employ a technique where each program can have $\frac{1}{4}$ million pages each of $\frac{1}{4}$ million bytes. This gives a program space of 64 megabytes, which is far larger than the total memory space the computer can support; hence the term virtual. The virtual space that is available to a program can be used to ensure the modularity of the program, especially of instructions and data.

4.9 Read only memories

So far the memories which have been discussed are ones which can be written to and read from. There is, however, a different sort of memory called read only memory (ROM) which can only be read from. Read only memories can be used to store algorithms (i.e. the instructions of a program) when the memory is manufactured, and once tested these algorithms should not need changing. Obviously algorithms which are going to be changed are not stored in ROM as this would be a very inefficient way of using a ROM. In general, once a ROM has been programmed it cannot be changed (see Section 4.10). ROM is therefore used for special kinds of computing machines which carry out dedicated tasks.

In general purpose computing machines, minis, mainframes and microcomputers ROM is often used to store part of the operating software of a computer system. When a computer is switched on there is nothing inside the RAM because such data is lost when the power is removed (see Section 4.10). It is therefore necessary to have a program which can be loaded automatically and which will then load the necessary programs into the main memory. Such a loading program is called a 'bootstrap' loader. The algorithm stored in the ROM is obeyed and reads other programs from a peripheral device. In most cases the program read in is part of the operating system which then controls the subsequent operation of the computer system.

In dedicated computers all the algorithms will be stored in a ROM, because the contents of the ROM are not destroyed when the power is switched off. An example of this would be a point of sale terminal (a glorified cash register). Such a terminal records the items being sold and the price payable, adds up the total and works out the change required for the cash tendered. Such a terminal can also be connected to a central computer which maintains stock control information. A dedicated computer will need some RAM, otherwise it could not store temporary data values, but there tends to be only a very little RAM in such a computer. This is in direct contrast to a general purpose computer where the amount of ROM is very small and is used to hold the program which will initially load the computer with its operating system. With the introduction of cheap robust microprocessors there has been a trend to incorporate these devices in hostile environments where traditionally constructed computers could not be used: for example, in machine tools or washing machines. Because these environments tend to be of a dedicated nature the use of ROM has increased significantly.

4.10 Memory technology

The technology of memory devices has progressed from magnetic techniques developed in the 1950s and 1960s to the semiconductor 'silicon chip' technology of the 1970s. This section will deal only with the semiconductor technology because no currently manufactured computing machines use magnetic techniques for main memory.

Early semiconductor memories could store only a few binary digits whereas modern memories can store hundreds of thousands of binary digits. This increase in capacity has been achieved by improvement in the technology of semiconductor devices. The original semiconductor technology was capable of building one transistor on a $\frac{1}{4}$ inch square of silicon (1960). By 1980 it became possible to build hundreds of thousands of transistors on the same size piece of silicon. The original discrete semiconductor memories were static memories. That is, once the memory had been written to, the information remained, provided that the power was not switched off. With the advent of integrated technology, dynamic memories were generated. A dynamic memory is one which has to be periodically refreshed, because the electric charge used to store the data slowly leaks away. This is analogous to a bucket with a hole in it: it is possible to say when the bucket is full and also when it is empty. There is an in-between stage where it is neither full nor empty. The refresh period ensures that all storage locations which should be full are filled up. The refresh mechanism takes place transparently and therefore the programmer is unaware that the process is taking place.

Read only memories are implemented in many different ways which give differing levels of flexibility. The simplest kind of ROM actually has the program built into it as the memory is manufactured. A more flexible approach is one which allows the ROM to be programmed by people other than the manufacturer. Such a programmable ROM (PROM) can be programmed by a special machine into which the desired program is previously read. Once the PROM has been programmed, it cannot be changed. A further level of sophistication is the erasable PROM (EPROM) which can be reprogrammed several times whilst retaining the read only characteristics of a ROM. Each type of ROM uses a type of semiconductor technology which allows the desired mode of operation. The PROM type uses the so called 'fusible link' which can be broken when a high enough current is passed through it. Initially, every bit is set to 1 and the programming requires that some of the links be changed to zero by breaking the appropriate fusible link. An EPROM uses the same technique, except that the fusible link can be regenerated when the EPROM is exposed to ultraviolet light. The access time of a memory, whether RAM or ROM, is the amount of time it takes to process the memory in order to read some data from or write some data into it. With the technology available at the start of the 1980s, the access time of memory varies from 30 ns to 1000 ns (1 ns = 10^{-9} s). As usual, the faster the memory the more expensive it is. Thus 30 ns memory is used for small high speed cache memories whereas 1000 ns memory is used for bulk memory.

4.11 Summary

This chapter has described how memories can be constructed and how they have developed from the original linear string of locations developed by

Von Neumann. Data is not normally just a linear string, it has other structures which have to be mapped on to a linear string. The development of large fast cheap memories has allowed designers to experiment with other memory strategies which try to overcome the restrictions of a linear string.

4.12 Problems

4.1 Why would a computer be equipped with 262 144 words rather than 250 000 or 275 000 which are much easier to remember?

4.2 Which of the following memories are possible? Which are reasonable? Explain.

	Bits in MAR	Cells in memory	Cell size in bits
a	10	1024	8
b	10	1024	12
c	9	1024	10
d	11	1024	10
e	10	10	1024
f	1024	10	10

4.3 Describe two ways in which a computer memory could be organized so as to allow individual words to be read only, read/write, or execute only?

4.4 Assuming an associative memory, as described in Section 4.4 having mask and interrogate registers, show the sequence of operations needed to evaluate not ((field 1 ≠ 2 and not field 2 = 3) or (field 3 = 1)) and field 4 = 0.

4.5 Explain how the principle of an interleaved memory can be used to increase access speed to a memory if the data part of the memory bus is wider than each memory cell.

4.6 Why is an hierarchy of memory types invaluable when designing a computer system?

4.7 Investigate how modern computers utilize memory techniques in their design. How has this improved the performance of each system?

4.8 Some implementations of paging do not use an associative memory, but instead maintain tables of the most recently used pages. These tables contain less entries than pages in real memory, the remainder being kept in main memory. Compare and contrast this with the technique described in Section 4.8.

4.9 In computers dedicated to a particular task the majority of memory is ROM. Why?

4.10 By reading other publications find out how the cost, speed and size of memory has varied over the past seven years.

5 Machine codes and addressing techniques

Chapter 1 introduced the general concept that both program instructions and data are stored in the main memory. This chapter will consider the structure of instructions stored in a computer, from the programmer's viewpoint.

Most instructions specify operations to be performed on data located either in the main memory or in general purpose registers in the central processing unit (CPU). The reference to this data, whether it be numeric or character data, is said to be the operand of the instruction.

5.1 Instruction formats

Any program involves a number of functionally different steps. Obviously the machine instructions will reflect the different functions. The functions can be roughly classed as:

- Data transfers between the main memory and the CPU registers
- Arithmetic and logic operations on data
- Program sequencing and control
- Input/output (I/O) transfers.

To examine possible formats for instructions, consider one of the fundamental instructions from the second of the above classes, an add instruction.

From the programmer's viewpoint, the simplest form of addition is C := A+B where A,B,C are the names of variables. Assume that the values of these three variables are stored in memory locations, their addresses being represented by the names A,B,C.

The above expression then has the following meaning. The contents of locations A and B are to be fetched into the CPU where they are added together using the arithmetic and logic unit (ALU). The resultant sum is then to be stored in location C.

If the whole of this expression is to be represented by one machine instruction, the machine instruction will need to contain three address fields (or three operands.)

This *3 address instruction* which could be represented symbolically as

Add A,B,C

would obviously require a large number of bits to accommodate three addresses.

An alternative is to use a *2 address instruction*. Here there are only going to be 2 address fields or operands (and consequently the instruction will occupy fewer bits) but there needs to be an implicit assumption about where the result is to be stored. The result is stored back in one of the operands, thus destroying its original value.

The instruction

Add A,B

could add the contents of addresses A and B, storing the sum in address A.

If it is important in a particular program, to ensure that the sum is placed in C, with the original values of A and B remaining unchanged then two instructions would have be used, namely:

Move C,B
Add C,A

This assumes that MOVE C,B performs the operation of copying the contents of address B to address C.

A further possibility is that of *1 address instructions*. Here, since there is only one operand, not only is there an implicit assumption about where the result is going to be stored, but also about where one of the operands is stored. Usually a general purpose CPU register, sometimes called an *accumulator* is used.

The sequence of instructions

LOAD   A
ADD   B
STORE   C

could perform the operation C := A+B. Here, the LOAD instruction copies the contents of address A into the accumulator, the ADD instruction adds the contents of address B into the accumulator and the STORE instruction copies the contents of the accumulator into address C.

Some computers have a number of general purpose registers which can be used as an accumulator, and in this case a second operand signifies the register to be used. However, since the number of bits to signify the register to be used (say 3 or 4 since there are often no more than 8 or 16 of such registers) is considerably less than would be necessary to signify a second memory address, these types of instructions are sometimes called *1½ address instructions*.

If a computer has a number of registers, there are usually some instructions to perform operations on data in registers only; that is, no reference is necessary to a main memory address. Since all operands are registers requiring only three or four bits each, these instructions obviously occupy only a small number of bits.

It is also possible to have instructions with no operands, and these are known as *zero address instructions*. Here the location of the operands is known implicitly. This will be discussed later in Section 5.5.

5.2 Instruction sets

All the machine instructions that are provided by a given computer are termed its *instruction set*.

Within the instruction set instructions can usually be classified into one of three types

(a) Memory reference instructions. These involve operations on data which is stored in memory.
(b) Non-memory reference instructions. These either require no data or operate on data stored within registers in the CPU.
(c) Input/output instructions (see Chapter 8).

5.2.1 *Memory reference instructions*

This class of instructions includes any instruction that references at least one location in memory, and consequently needs to hold the address of that location within the instruction.

It is not possible to give a definitive list of instructions that are available on any computer, since a computer manufacturer will design and provide a set of instructions that arise partly from other architectural considerations (for example, word size and available registers) and partly as a result of what he thinks is 'useful' in relation to the environment in which the computer is to be used. However, the following list is typical of memory reference instructions that may be found on a computer.

1 Load a register with the contents of a memory location.
2 Store the contents of a register into a memory location.
3 Add the contents of a memory location to those of a register.
4 Subtract the contents of a memory location from those of a register.
5 Compare the contents of a register with that of a memory location, skipping the next instruction if they are unequal.
6 Increment the content of a memory location and skip the next instruction if the result is zero.
7 Combine the contents of a memory location with those of a register by performing a logical operation on the corresponding bits (AND, OR, Exclusive OR).

8 Branch instructions—unconditional jump, conditional jumps and jumps to subroutines.
9 Shift instructions—a group of instructions which moves all the bits in a memory location either to the left or to the right with bits either being 'lost' off one end or coming back in at the other end of the memory location.

To examine the format of an instruction, consider a one address computer which has two general purpose registers (these could be called the A register and B register) and a memory word size of 16 bits. Typical instructions would be 'Load to A' (transfer the contents of a word in memory to the A register) or 'Add to A' (add the contents of a word in memory to the A register).

The layout of such an instruction (e.g. a Hewlett-Packard 21MX computer) could be as shown in Fig. 5.1.

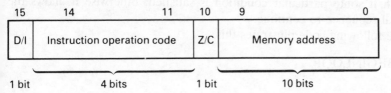

Fig. 5.1

In a one address machine the basic content of an instruction is the operation code which identifies that instruction and the address in memory of the word that contains the data being manipulated. As can be seen above, the operation code occupies four bits and the memory address ten bits. The purpose of bits 10 and 15 will become clear shortly.

If the address of the word in memory being referred to by this instruction can occupy a maximum of ten bits, the largest address that can be referred to would be

$$2^{10} - 1 = 1023$$

Hence addresses can range between 0 and 1023; that is 1024 addresses.

Most computers, however, have memories much larger than this. If we allowed a computer to have a memory with a maximum size of, say, one million units of storage (words or bytes) then 20 bits would be needed for the address of a data item. This would make the instructions much larger and inevitably there would be a requirement for even larger memories.

To overcome this problem there is usually a limit to the number of words that can be *directly* addressed; that is, the instruction contains the absolute address of the data word in memory. To address other parts of the memory, other addressing techniques have to be used (see Section 5.3).

5.2.2 *Branching*

Not all memory reference instructions are in fact manipulating data stored in memory addresses. There is a requirement for a class of instructions, known as branch instructions, which refer to a memory address for the purpose of transferring control to this address.

The simplest form of branch instruction, an unconditional branch, can be represented symbolically as in the following code sequence.

> BEGINLOOP Add (to a register) contents of X;
> Branch to BEGINLOOP;

The branch instruction interrupts the normal sequence of instructions and causes control to return to the instruction at label BEGINLOOP. Obviously, this particular loop is an unending loop. Control is always going to return to BEGINLOOP. It is more usual for a branch instruction only to branch if some particular condition is satisfied; otherwise it allows the normal sequence to continue.

The following code illustrates this.

> BEGINLOOP   .
>
> .
>
> .
>
> .
>
> .
>
> Decrement register A;
> Branch >0   BEGINLOOP;

The DECREMENT instruction would decrement the contents of register A (which would originally have been set to an initial value, say n) by 1 each time through the loop.

In the branch instruction, the condition under which branching occurs or not is usually related to the result of an arithmetic or logic operation. In the above example the condition is that the result of the most recent arithmetic operation is greater than 0. Since the DECREMENT instruction immediately precedes the branch, this means that a branch to BEGINLOOP will occur as long as the contents of register A remain greater than 0. After the loop has been executed n times, the register A will have been decremented to 0 and the branch will not occur.

Figure 5.2 illustrates a simple loop to add up a series of numbers stored in locations NUM1, NUM2 . . . NUMn.

This also illustrates an alternative way of controlling a loop. An 'increment and skip if zero' instruction increments a particular register by 1 and if the value then becomes equal to zero, control will skip around the next sequential instruction to the one after. Consequently, in the above

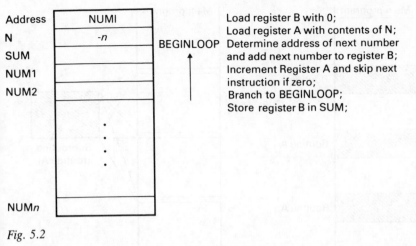

Fig. 5.2

example, while the A register contains a negative value, control will arrive at the branch instruction and then transfer back to BEGINLOOP. When the A register reaches the value zero, after n loops, control will skip around the branch instruction and continue with the store instruction.

5.2.3 Subroutines

A special form of branching or instruction sequencing is often necessary, when, for example, a particular task has to be performed a number of times on different data values. Instead of including the code each time it is required, it can be written as a subroutine and included only once as shown in Fig. 5.3.

A special form of branch instruction is used to transfer control to the subroutine each time it is needed. At the completion of the subroutine, control must be transferred back to where it was 'called' from, so that processing can continue.

The need for a special form of branch instruction arises because it is necessary to save the address of the next instruction in the main program, after the branch instruction, so that control can return to this point.

An example of such an instruction is a jump to subroutine instruction illustrated in Fig. 5.4. Here, the jump to subroutine (JSB) instruction stores the address of the next instruction following it (RETURN) in the first word of the subroutine (SUB); it then commences execution of the instruction stored in the second word of the subroutine and continues the normal sequencing.

On completion of the subroutine, an *indirect* jump to SUB is required (see Section 5.3.2 for an explanation of an indirect address) which will in this case then transfer control to RETURN.

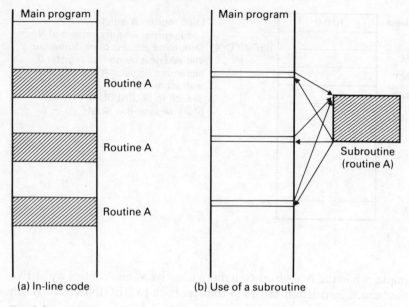

(a) In-line code   (b) Use of a subroutine

Fig. 5.3

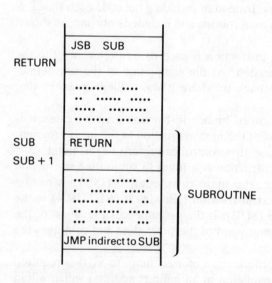

Fig. 5.4

5.2.4 *Non memory reference and input/output instructions*

A non memory reference instruction is one that does not need to contain an address of a memory location. Typical of such instructions are those that operate on data stored in registers. Because most computers have relatively few registers, it is only necessary to allocate three or four bits at the most to indicate the register being used; consequently these instructions are relatively short. The following is typical of such instructions.

(a) Register to register arithmetic and logical instructions such as ADD, SUBTRACT, MOVE, AND, OR, EXCLUSIVE OR. The logical instructions allow the programmer to isolate individual bits within a word. For example, an AND operation allows the modification of some bits such that certain of them remain as they are and others are set to zero. An OR operation allows the modification of some bits such that certain of them remain as they are and others are set to one, whereas the EXCLUSIVE OR operation selectively reverses the values of bits.

(b) Shift instructions. This is usually a group of instructions which move all the bits in a register either to the left or to the right with bits either being 'lost' off the end or coming back in at the other end of the register.

As an example of the use of logical and shift instructions consider the following example. Suppose an eight bit word W is composed of three fields, a two bit field IND, a four bit field X and a two bit field Y in that order. It is required to retrieve field X and put it in a register by itself.

The following instructions would achieve this, assuming that the MASK word contains the bit pattern: 00111100

> Load register R with the MASK;
> AND register R with the word W leaving the result in R;
> Shift right register R 2 places.

The contents of register R at the end of each of the above steps is

> 00111100
> 00field X00
> 0000field X

This particular example could also be achieved by just two shift instructions:

> Shift left register R 2 places
> Shift right register R 4 places

It is left to the reader to verify this.

5.3 Memory addressing

As was indicated in Section 5.2.1, there is a need for more than one way of obtaining the address of a word in memory for an instruction, because of the length restrictions associated with the most obvious way of including an address in an instruction.

The effective address of an operand is the address that is used to access the memory, once all transformations and modifications have been carried out. We shall now consider some modification techniques.

5.3.1 *Direct (absolute) address*

The effective address of the location of the operand is given explicitly as part of the instruction.

This usually places restrictions on the range of words that can be addressed in this way, depending on the number of bits allocated for the address within the instruction.

5.3.2 *Indirect address*

The effective address of the operand is stored in the main memory location whose address is in the instruction or in the register, if the operand of the instruction is a register rather than a memory address.

The purpose of bit 15 in the instruction layout defined in Section 5.2.1 is to indicate whether the address field in the instruction is the absolute address of the operand or the address of a location in memory which contains the absolute address of the operand. It would be set to 0 if direct addressing was being used, and to 1 if indirect addressing was specified.

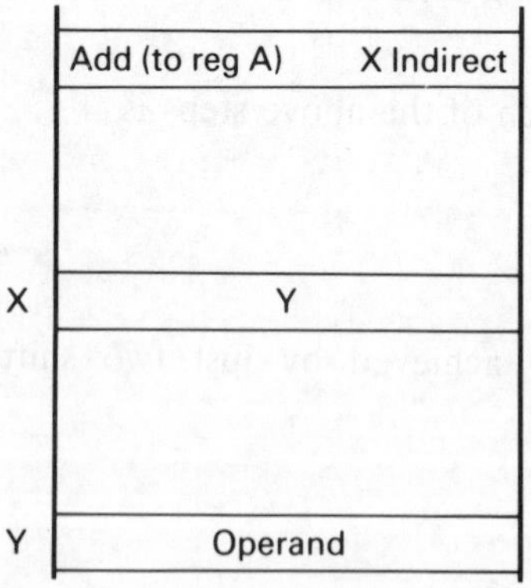

Fig. 5.5

The advantage of indirect addressing in this context is that the memory location which contains the absolute address of the data can use all of its bits to indicate the address, whereas only the address field is available in the instruction, the other bits being used to define the operation code and other necessary information.

Figure 5.5 gives an example of indirect addressing. The execution of the ADD instruction starts by fetching the contents of location X from the main memory. The value, Y, is the absolute address of the operand and is then used to fetch the operand from the memory.

Figure 5.6 repeats the program given earlier (in Section 5.2.2) for summing a series of values stored in consecutive locations but using

	Load Register B with 0;
	Load Register A with contents of N;
BEGINLOOP	Add to Register B contents of ADDR (indirect);
	Increment ADDR;
	Increment Register A and skip next instruction if zero;
	Branch to BEGINLOOP;
	Store Register B in SUM;

Fig. 5.6

indirect addressing. ADDR is a location containing initially the address of location NUM1; subsequently the contents of ADDR are incremented by 1 to step through the consecutive words containing the values to be added.

5.3.3 *Immediate address*

The operand is given explicitly in the instruction rather than the address of where the operand is. This can be useful for dealing with data items that have fixed values but again, the size of the constant is limited by the number of bits available for the operand.

5.3.4 *Index addressing*

The effective address of the operand is calculated by adding an additional value, the *index value*, to the address given in the instruction.

The index value is usually stored within a CPU register. On some computers this may be a dedicated register known as the index register. On other computers it may be any one of the general purpose registers provided.

Figure 5.7 illustrates the use of the index register, assuming there is only one dedicated index register. The instruction operand refers to address S,

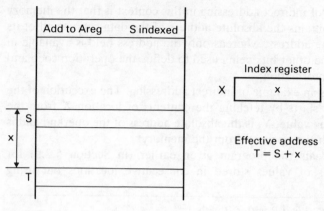

Fig. 5.7

but because indexing is specified the effective address is address S plus the contents of the index register. By varying the contents of the index register, the same instruction can be made to refer to a number of addresses. This is a similar facility to that of subscripting within a high level programming language.

Figure 5.8 repeats the previous example which sums the contents of a series of consecutive words, but using indexing.

	Load Register B with 0;
	Load Register A with contents of N;
	Set X to zero;
BEGINLOOP	Add to Register B NUM1 indexed by X;
	Increment X;
	Increment Register A and skip next instruction if zero;
	Branch to BEGINLOOP;
	Store Register B in SUM;

Fig. 5.8

5.4 Addressing mechanisms

In addition to the addressing techniques that have just been described, all computer systems impose some fundamental addressing mechanism on the programmer in order either to minimize the number of address bits required in an instruction or to allow relocatability of programs. Relocation is the ability to move a machine code program from one area of store to another, without invalidating all the addresses.

We now examine some different mechanisms provided by computer manufacturers.

5.4.1 *Base and current page addressing mechanism*

The memory of a computer equipped with this type of mechanism is logically (*not* physically) divided into regions of a fixed length called pages. Take for example a 16 bit word machine with memory reference instructions of the form indicated in Section 5.2.1. The memory could be divided logically into pages of 1024 words each. A page is defined as the largest block of memory that can be directly addressed by the memory address bits of a memory reference instruction. In this particular example the memory reference instructions have 10 bits to specify a memory address; thus the page size is 1024 locations.

Provision is made to address directly one of two pages: page zero (the base page) and the current page (the page in which the instruction itself is located). The memory reference instructions include a bit (bit 10) reserved to specify one or other of those two pages. To address locations in any other page, indirect addressing would have to be used.

The advantages of this mechanism are twofold. First the number of bits required for the address within an instruction is kept down to 10 bits plus one bit to indicate base or current page and secondly, all direct addresses are actually relative either to absolute location zero, if on base page, or relative to the start of the page in which the instruction is located. Thus a program may be located or relocated on to any page of memory and the address fields are still valid.

5.4.2 *Base addressing mechanism*

On many computers, instead of storing any form of address within the instruction, all that is stored in the instruction itself is the number of a register, the actual address being stored in the register.

Consider for example the addressing mechanism on a PDP-11 computer. A 16 bit instruction is divided into two fields. The OP-code field is 10 bits long, leaving 6 bits for the address field.

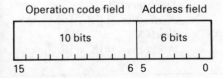

Operation code field Address field

| 10 bits | 6 bits |

15   6 5   0

The address field obviously cannot hold a useful actual address but is used to reference a register in various ways. The rightmost 3 bit field specifies one of eight registers R0 to R7. The other 3 bit field defines how the address in the specified register is to be treated. In addition to direct or indirect addressing this allows four basic addressing modes.

(1) *Register mode*. The operand is the contents of the register specified. In the indirect version, the specified register contains the effective address of the operand.

(2) *Autoincrement mode*. The effective address is in the specified register. After the operand has been fetched, the contents of the specified register is automatically incremented. In the indirect case, the effective address is contained in the memory location pointed at by the specified register.

(3) *Autodecrement mode*. The contents of the specified register are decremented and then used as the effective address, or as a pointer to the address in a memory location, in the indirect case.

(4) *Index mode*. The effective address is generated by adding the contents of the specified register to the value X which is contained in the word immediately following the instruction. If indirection is specified, it is performed after indexing.

Table 5.1 summarizes these addressing modes.

Table 5.1 Addressing modes

Bits in address field			Mode	Meaning
b5	b4	b3		
0	0	0	Register	A effective = R_n
				(i.e. operand = $[R_n]$)
0	1	0	Autoincrement	A effective = $[R_n]$
				Increment R_n
1	0	0	Autodecrement	Decrement R_n
				A effective = $[R_n]$
1	1	0	Index	Fetch X
				A effective = $X + [R_n]$
0	0	1	Register indirect	A effective = $[R_n]$
0	1	1	Autoincrement indirect	A effective = $[[R_n]]$
				Increment R_n
1	0	1	Autodecrement indirect	Decrement R_n
				A effective = $[[R_n]]$
1	1	1	Index indirect	Fetch X
				A effective = $[X + [R_n]]$

where [ ] means 'the contents of'.

5.4.3 *Base and displacement addressing mechanism*

The two previous sections have given examples of addressing mechanisms used on computers of relatively small word length (16 bits). Many large computer systems are designed with large memory space in mind and consequently have a larger word length. A typical range for the word length in a large computer is from 32 to 64 bits. In this environment it is easier to store addresses within an instruction. However, having more bits available within an instruction may lead to the decision to have two address instructions rather than simply larger address fields. As an example of the addressing mechanism on a large computer system, consider the instruction formats used in the IBM 370 series of computers.

This series resembles the PDP-11 minicomputer in that the base point for an address is the contents of some register. The IBM 370 computers have sixteen 32 bit general purpose registers that may be used for this function.

A program must arrange for one of these registers to contain the address of some convenient point in memory. An address within an instruction is then represented by two fields. A base field (4 bits long) defines the register which contains this 'base address' R_b. A displacement field D (12 bits long) contains a value representing the distance in bytes that the required operand is from this base address.

The effective address of an operand then becomes

$$A \text{ effective} = [R_b] + D$$

Although registers are 32 bits long, the effective address is computed by using only 24 bits but this permits accessing up to 2^{24} locations or approximately 16 million bytes of store.

The inclusion of the base register serves to assist relocatability of some programs. In a large computer, it is common to have several programs residing in the main memory at the same time. In this environment it is desirable that a program and its associated data can be moved into any available space in memory. In the case of the base and displacement addressing mechanism, a complete program can be located anywhere in the memory and executed correctly, simply by loading an appropriate address value into the base register. Thus the value of the base register needs to be set only once, at the start of each program.

Within the instruction set of the IBM 370 series of computers, some instructions also allow an index register to be specified. This is simply another of the 16 general purpose registers R_x whose contents are also added to the address generated from the base register contents and the displacement. Thus the effective address of the operand then becomes

$$A \text{ effective} = [R_b] + D + [R_x]$$

The IBM 370 series of computers do not have indirect addressing facilities but this is not necessarily a drawback since indexed addressing can normally be substituted.

The fact that an address within an instruction is made up of a total of 16 bits on the IBM 370, and that the word length is 32 bits leads to an interesting point. A register to register instruction (non memory reference) would only need 8 bits for the operation code (on the IBM 370 computers all op-codes are 8 bits) and 4 bits for each of the two register operands. Hence this class of instructions only requires half a word. Register/storage instructions, one operand being a register the other a store address, need at least 8 + 4 + 16 bits and therefore will require a full word. Storage/storage instructions, both operands being store addresses, require at least 8 + 16 + 16 bits (i.e. 40 bits) and therefore will need one and a half words.

Not all the instructions therefore, are of the same length and some require more than one word. This variable length instruction format is quite common, and found in a number of computers.

5.5 Stack computers

In the previous discussion on memory accessing, it has been assumed that an instruction could access any location in memory merely by quoting its address. A stack (sometimes called a pushdown stack) is a list of data elements, usually either words or bytes, with the accessing restriction that items of data can only be added or removed at one end of the list. The term stack arises from the analogy with, say, a pile (or stack) of plates. New plates can only be added on to the top of the pile, and the only plate that can be removed is that on the top of the pile which was in fact the last to be added to the pile. This gives rise to another common term for a stack, LIFO meaning 'last in first out'.

5.5.1 *The organization of a stack*

A stack can be organized as part of the memory with successive items in the stack occupying successive memory locations. A 'stack computer' is one whose machine instruction set provides specific instructions for manipulating data stored in stack form. Figure 5.9 shows how a stack could be organized in memory.

SP, SL, SB are three registers containing addresses of memory locations as shown. The stack pointer (SP) is the address of the last data item to be entered into the stack. Since the stack is usually just a part of memory, it is important that no attempt is made to remove items from the stack when it is empty, or to add new items to the stack when it is full; otherwise memory locations will be accessed that are not part of the stack and will consequently be using invalid information. Hence, there are registers containing the address of the stack base (SB, the address of the first location of the stack) and the stack limit (SL, the address of the last location of the stack area).

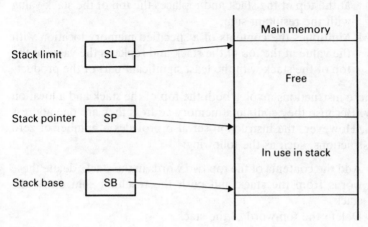

Fig. 5.9

5.5.2 *Stack instructions*

The basic operations on a stack are those of putting a data item on to the stack (known as PUSH) or taking a data item off the stack (known as POP).

The machine instruction PUSH needs to carry out the following tasks:

(a) increment the contents of the stack pointer register.
(b) check that this value is not now beyond the limit of the stack area.
(c) insert the required data item on to the stack.

The machine instruction POP performs the following tasks:

(a) removes from the stack the data pointed to by the stack pointer
(b) decrements the stack pointer.
(c) checks that the stack pointer is now not below the base of the stack area.

Some computers provide further instructions to perform arithmetic operations directly with the top two elements of the stack.

Consider the following instructions taken from the instruction set of the Hewlett-Packard HP3000 computer, which provides extensive stack facilities.

LOAD Performs a PUSH operation of a specified memory word on to the stack.

STOR Performs a POP operation taking the top element off the stack and storing it in a specified memory location.

ADDM Adds the contents of a specified memory location to the value at the top of the stack and replaces the top of the stack value with the resultant sum.

MPYM Multiplies the contents of a specified memory location with the value at the top of the stack and replaces the value at the top of the stack with the least significant part of the product.

All of these instructions involve both the top of the stack and a location in memory. Because they contain a memory address they are one address instruction. However, the instruction set also provides a number of zero address instructions, such as the following:

ADD Add the contents of the top two words in the stack, delete these words from the stack and push the resultant sum on to the stack.

DEL Delete the top word of the stack.

Because there is no address to be stored in the instruction, these instructions will merely consist of an operation code and can therefore be much shorter. The approach taken on the HP 3000 computer is to 'pack' two operations, where possible, into a word. Instructions normally occupy one word (16 bits): 4 bits for the op-code leaving 12 bits for the other appropriate information.

The zero address stack instructions are identified by an op-code of four zeros, the other 12 bits being split into two 6 bit fields each being a 'stack op-code' specifying a stack instruction.

The second 6 bit field for specifying a second stack operation can only be used to advantage when two consecutive stack operations are specified. In other cases this part of the instruction remains unused.

In order to speed up the operation of such stack instructions, not all of the stack needs to be in main memory. Accessing of main memory locations is one of the most critical time constraints as far as the operation of the central processing unit is concerned. The time needed to fetch an item from main memory, or to write an item to main memory tends to be very long compared with the time required for operations within the CPU, for example the transfer of data between registers. To hold all of the stack within registers would be expensive and would be an inflexible use of the registers. However, it is possible for the top few elements of the stack to be resident within registers, the remainder of the stack being stored in main memory. This certainly speeds up the operation on the top elements of the stack, and can be implemented so that the programmer need not be aware of the fact. On the HP 3000 computer there are four registers containing the top four elements of the stack. The remainder of the stack is stored in main memory, data being transferred into the fourth register as necessary.

5.5.3 *Use of stacks*

A stack is one of a number of data structures that are of interest in computing science and can be used in the solution of a number of problems. Two examples of the use of stacks are given here.

A stack can be used in connection with subroutine linkage. Section 5.2.3 explained the need for storing the address of the location following the instruction that branched to the subroutine, in order to allow control to return to this address, and processing to continue.

Since it is a reasonable and practical programming technique to allow one subroutine to call another, it is obviously important that each return address is stored separately so that addresses can be retrieved when necessary. The situation where one subroutine calls a second subroutine could obviously be extended to allow this second subroutine to call a third. This process is known as subroutine nesting and can be carried out to any depth. Eventually, of course, the last subroutine completes its processing and returns to the subroutine that called it. It is important here to note that the return address required will be the last one to be stored. That is, the return addresses are stored and recalled in a last-in-first-out order. This naturally suggests that these addresses could be PUSHed on to a stack and POPed off as required.

A stack facility is also useful for storing intermediate results when evaluating arithmetic expressions. Consider the following example, illustrated in Fig. 5.10. Assume that the values of the variables A,B,C,D,E are not stored in the stack initially but are stored in memory locations with addresses denoted by A,B,C,D,E.

$$X = (A + B) * C + D * E$$

The machine instructions necessary to perform the above computation (using the HP 3000 instruction set defined in Section 5.5.2) are:

Step 1	LOAD	A
2	ADDM	B
3	MPYM	C
4	LOAD	D
5	MPYM	E
6	ADD	
7	STOR	X

Fig. 5.10

At the completion of Step 3 the top of the stack will contain the value of (A + B) * C. This will then be pushed down the stack as D is loaded on to the stack. At the completion of Step 5 the top of the stack contains the value of D*E. The operation of Step 6 adds the top two elements of the stack together, leaving the result at the top of the stack, which is then stored in location X in memory.

The stack then has provided a convenient facility for the temporary storage of intermediate results. Further, if the top few elements of the stack are actually CPU registers (as described in Section 5.5.2), the above arithmetic operations are taking place using registers, which will take significantly less time than the equivalent operations on memory locations.

5.6 Instruction sets in microprocessors

Historically, microprocessors and microcomputers appear to have been developed as something 'different' from minicomputers or mainframe computers. So far as their instruction sets are concerned, however, they are no different. Most microcomputers have extensive instruction sets, making them truly general purpose processors. On earlier microprocessors with only an 8 bit word length, formation of addresses was difficult without recourse to addressing mechanisms such as those described here or even more complex ones. Because of these addressing difficulties, two address instructions were difficult to accommodate; so most machines adopt a one address instruction type.

On the more recent types of microcomputer with 16 bit word length the problems are no different from those of any computer with a 16 bit word length and so all of the techniques described in this chapter are appropriate.

5.7 Summary

The principal purpose of this chapter has been to introduce the representation of instructions at the machine code level as seen by the programmer and to discuss the problems of addressing memory locations.

A major point in the study of a particular computer is the method used for addressing memory locations. Inevitably the addressing scheme depends on the word length. Computers with a relatively short word length have to employ a more complex addressing mechanism and are, in general, less able to address a very large memory without resorting to multiple word instructions. The disadvantage of this is that it takes longer to process such instructions because they require multiple accesses to memory just to fetch the instruction. The instruction set is also dependent on word length, since the variety of instructions will depend on the utilization of the bit space within each instruction. Instruction formats range from those with two operations within one word (some stack instructions) to those whose instructions require two or even three words each.

Examples of both instruction sets and addressing mechanisms have been drawn from a variety of machines and should, at least, indicate that there is no single approach to the problem but that each manufacturer decides for himself what he feels is appropriate both functionally and financially.

In order to understand thoroughly the main principles explained in this chapter it is necessary to write some simple programs in machine code or, perhaps, assembler code and examine the machine code version, for a particular computing machine. The differences between various computers can be readily understood once the common basic principles have been grasped.

5.8 Problems

5.1 (a) Explain what is meant by
  (1) a zero addressing machine
  (2) a one address machine
  (3) a two address machine
  (4) a three address machine
  indicating how the presence or absence of addresses is utilized and how the machine code reflects the machine structure.
  (b) What is an effective address? How is it achieved when addressing
  (1) directly
  (2) by indexing
  (3) indirectly
  Indicate further how indirect and indexed addressing can be combined.

5.2 Explain what is meant by the following terms:
  (a) The effective address
  (b) The addressing mode
  Describe two simple addressing modes in common use. Specify their advantages and disadvantages and give a specific detailed example of each mode from a computer you are familiar with. Use diagrams where appropriate.

5.3 (a) What factors have to be taken into account when the number of operands in an instruction is being specified and how does this affect the computer's architecture?

(b) Describe four ways in which an effective address can be generated.

5.4 (a) Explain the difference between BALR and USING statements in IBM 370 Assembler language clearly indicating the effect of each at assembly and execution time.

(b) What is the machine code (in hexadecimal) corresponding to the move instructions in the following 370 Assembler language programs.

```
(1)         START    0
     BEG    BALR     11,0
            USING    *,11

            MVC      A,B
            MVC      B(3),A
            MVC      C,A
     A      DS       CL5
     B      DS       CL5
     C      DS       CL4
            END      BEG

(2)         START    256
     TOP    BALR     9,0
            USING    *,9
            MVC      A(2),B
     A      DC       CL6
     B      DC       CL6
            END      TOP
```

(c) Write down 370 Assembler coding to exchange the contents of two general registers without requiring an intermediate storage location.

(d) Describe the linkage conventions when writing subroutines in 370 Assembler, indicating the advantages of having such conventions.

5.5 (a) Explain the function of the base register in the addressing mechanism of the IBM 370 machine instructions.

(b) Explain the term indexing in IBM 370 Assembler code.

(c) Write down the machine code that will be generated for the instructions in the following IBM 370 Assembler language program and explain the purpose of the program.

```
            START    0
     INDEX  BALR     15,0
            USING    *,15
```

```
              L            10,CZERO
              L            11,CZERO
              L            12,CFOUR
              L            13,CSTOP
LOOP          A            10,V(11)
              BXLE         11,12,LOOP
OUT           ST           10,W
              BR           14
CZERO         DC           F'0'
CFOUR         DC           F'4'
CSTOP         DC           F'396'
W             DS           F
V             DS           100F
              END
```

5.6 Show with examples how logical and shift operations can be used
   (a) to replace part of a binary pattern by zeros leaving the rest
       unchanged
   (b) to test for the occurrence of a 3 bit pattern in a particular part
       of a word or byte
   (c) to pack a 5 bit pattern which is right justified in a register,
       into bits 8 to 12 of the word labelled ODD.

5.7 (a) Explain how machine instructions refer to operands held in
       the main memory of an IBM 370 computer. Include in your
       explanation the use of indexing.
   (b) Explain the purpose of the instructions
       BALR   r12, 0
       USING *, r12
       that are often coded at the start of an assembler language
       program.

5.8 Discuss the relative merits of the addressing methods available in
    the PDP-11 and IBM 370 computers. In particular, discuss how
    the addressing method in each machine facilitates the following:
    relocatability, implementation of a stack, accessing an operand
    list.

5.9 IBM 370 computers do not have indirect addressing. Assuming
    that the address of an operand is stored in main memory, how
    would you access this operand?

*The following exercises can be done by using either the machine code of a
computer you have access to, or the simulator STARTLE (see Appendix 2)
with the predefined machines such as SOATM, INDOAM, SSTM.*

5.10 Write a machine code program to compare two words in the main
     memory. If they are the same, set up 0 in a register and halt. If
     they are different set up 1 in the register and halt.

5.11 Two numbers stored in consecutive words in memory are to be multiplied together and the answer placed in the next word. The numbers to be multiplied are such that the resultant value can be contained in a single word. However, there is no multiply instruction and therefore it will have to be done, as efficiently as possible, using other instructions. Write and test the program.

5.12 Set up a table of numbers in consecutive addresses. Write and test a program which, with use of a loop, will add together this list of numbers, and store the result in a further memory location.

5.13 Write a machine code program to evaluate the following expression:

$$W = (A + B)/(C/D + E*F/(G + H))$$

5.14 (a) Describe how you could organize a stack within a computer which had two registers available for holding the top two elements of the stack, the remainder being held in main memory.

(b) Write algorithms for code to PUSH and POP items to and from the above stack.

(c) Write and test the code for the above algorithms.

6 The central processing unit

The previous chapter has described the requirement for and the structure of machine instructions. In order for the instructions to be obeyed there must be a unit that will fetch each instruction in turn from the memory, examine it and arrange for the appropriate action to be taken. This is the Central Processing Unit (CPU).

The solution to any problem is defined by an algorithm. This algorithm is then broken down further into a sequence of steps (that must be obeyed in that particular sequence) known as the machine code instructions. The CPU adopts the same approach. In order for it to fetch and execute a particular instruction it must perform a sequence of more rudimentary operations in a particular order. The operations and the means by which they occur will be described in this chapter.

6.1 Component parts

The CPU can be thought of as being made up of a number of component parts. These are illustrated in Fig. 6.1. There are a number of special purpose registers (in addition to the general purpose registers that are available to the programmer), an Arithmetic and Logic Unit (ALU) which can be thought of as a 'black box' which performs actual computations, and a control unit which is effectively the nerve centre of the machine, sending control signals to all other units.

6.1.1 *Internal registers*

A program is made up of a series of instructions stored in the main memory of the computer. To execute this program, the CPU fetches the instructions one at a time and arranges for the appropriate actions to be performed. Instructions are fetched from consecutive locations unless a branch instruction of some form indicates that the next instruction to be executed is stored somewhere else.

As we saw in Chapter 4, all communication with the memory is done via the two registers Memory Address Register (MAR) and Memory Buffer Register (MBR). In order to fetch the next instruction, the CPU has to

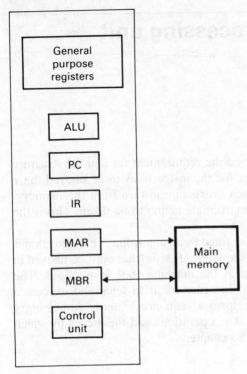

Fig. 6.1

place its address in the MAR and issue a read memory command, as a result of which the instruction will be fetched and placed in the MBR. Having fetched it, the CPU may have to reference memory again to execute it if, for example, it is a memory reference instruction that requires data to be fetched from memory. To fetch the data the CPU will have to place the address of the data in the MAR and this will, of course, destroy the address of this current instruction which is stored in the MAR. The CPU would not know, therefore, the address of the next instruction.

Consequently there is a need for a register to be dedicated to the task of keeping the address of the next instruction to be executed. This is known as the Program Counter (PC). The PC register is initially loaded with the address in memory of the location of the first instruction of the program, and then, after each instruction has been fetched, it is incremented to point to the next location, unless the instruction is a branch instruction.

When an instruction has been fetched from the memory it will be left in the MBR. However, since the control section of the CPU will need to have access to the instruction during execution, and the MBR may be needed for data during execution, in a memory reference instruction for example, it is also necessary to have a register dedicated to holding the current instruction being executed. This register is known as the Instruction Register (IR).

A program then, is obeyed by the CPU carrying out the following sequence of events:

(a) Copy PC contents into the MAR and initiate the memory read
(b) Increment the PC
(c) Copy the instruction now in the MBR into the IR
(d) Decode the IR (i.e., examine the instruction to determine what instruction it is)
(e) Execute the instruction
(f) Repeat from step (a).

This can be represented by a symbolic notation as follows, where [x] means 'contents of x', and M represents a main memory location.

[PC]   → MAR
[M]   → MBR
[PC] +1   → PC
[MBR]   → IR
Decode IR
Execute the instruction.

The 'Decode IR' step is achieved by means of a decoder. This is essentially circuitry which examines the operation code field of the instruction in the IR and outputs a signal that indicates which particular instruction is being requested.

Obviously step (e) above also consists of a number of steps, depending on the instruction, and this will be examined in Section 6.2.

6.1.2 *The arithmetic and logic unit*

The arithmetic and logic unit (ALU) is that part of the CPU where all the arithmetical and logical operations are performed. Constructed from high speed electronic components, it is a sophisticated piece of circuitry which will perform some specified operation on the data presented to its inputs. Typical of the operations that an ALU is able to perform are

(a) Arithmetic operations such as ADD and COMPLEMENT
(b) Logical operations, such as AND, OR, EXCLUSIVE OR
(c) Manipulation operations such as SHIFT, TEST.

Note that specific details of number systems, sign conventions and their manipulation are given in Appendix 1.

The arithmetic operations to be found in any ALU are basically those of add and one's complement. Subtraction is usually performed by taking two's complement of the number to be subtracted (one's complement plus one) and adding it to the other value. Multiply and divide operations are much more complex than either addition or subtraction. On some machines these operations are provided at the machine instruction level and on other machines both multiply and divide are supplied as software routines. These routines basically implement multiplication as a sequence of adds and shifts, and division as a sequence of subtracts and shifts.

Logical operations provided are usually those of AND, OR, EXCLU-SIVE OR (see Section 5.2.4).

The type of shift instructions provided are also discussed in Section 5.2.4 and are essentially of two kinds, arithmetic or shift and rotate. The rotate instructions are shift instructions where the bits that disappear off one end of the word come back in at the other end of the word. An arithmetic shift is one which preserves the sign bit. The test operations provide the facility for testing the relative size of values, although the operations themselves are usually simple arithmetic ones. There are often a number of single bit registers (flip flops) associated with the ALU which can be set as a result of an arithmetic operation. Examples of these are N bit, Z bit, O bit, set to binary 1 if the result of an arithmetic operation is negative, zero, or results in overflow respectively. The registers can then be tested by instructions to determine conditional jumps in the program sequence. For example, to determine the relative sizes of A and B, the operation $A - B$ is performed.

Instead of the normal value of $A - B$ being output by the ALU, it will merely set the values of the N bit and the Z bit to appropriate values. If A > B then N = 0 and Z = 0. If A = B then N = 0 and Z = 1. If A < B then N = 1 and Z = 0.

6.1.3 *Floating point unit*

The provision of floating point arithmetic in a computing machine is of great convenience to a lot of users. Apart from having an extended range of values available, the fact that the programmer does not have to worry about scale factors and aligning binary points is an important aspect.

However, the implementation of a floating point unit can be expensive. One way to reduce the cost is to provide the facilities by software routines, but these routines may require hundreds of main memory locations to store instructions and data tables.

In machines where the use of floating point arithmetic is to play a significant part, it is usually provided by an additional hardware feature, the Floating Point Unit. Although the FPU is expensive, it can reduce execution times significantly when compared with software implementations.

6.2 Execution of a complete instruction

As we saw in Section 6.1.1, a program stored in the main memory of a computer is obeyed by the CPU carrying out the following sequence of events, described with use of the symbolic notation introduced earlier.

(a) [PC]   → MAR
(b) [M]   → MBR
(c) [PC] + 1   → PC
(d) [MBR]   → IR
(e) Decode   IR
(f) Execute this instruction
(g) Repeat from step (a).

By examining this sequence it can be seen that steps (a) to (e) are concerned with FETCHing the instruction from the main memory, and that step (f) is concerned with EXECUTing this instruction. Each of these steps is called a micro-instruction.

These two stages are known as the *fetch phase* and the *execute phase*, or alternatively the *fetch/execute cycle*. Obviously the fetch phase is the same, regardless of what instruction is being fetched, although if an instruction occupies more than one main memory location, the fetch phase will have to be repeated as many times as necessary to fetch the complete instruction. The execute phase however, is dependent on the particular instruction. To examine the sort of sequence necessary in the execute phase, consider the following instruction types.

6.2.1 *Execution of a non memory reference instruction*

The execution phase of a non memory reference instruction is straightforward in that it does not require any information to be fetched from main memory. We noted in Section 5.2.4 that these are often instructions which manipulate data stored in a CPU register. In this case, all that is required is to present to the ALU the bits in the particular register defined and the signal from the decoder which indicates what particular action is required. When the ALU has completed its task, the resulting bit pattern will be left in the appropriate register.

6.2.2 *Execution of a memory reference instruction*

In this case, the execution phase is a little more involved, because a memory read is required to fetch the appropriate data from memory before the required actions can be carried out. The execute phase for an instruction which fetches some data from memory and performs some arithmetic on it can be represented symbolically as follows

$$[IR]_{address} \rightarrow MAR$$
$$\text{field}$$

$$[M] \rightarrow \quad MBR$$

Perform appropriate action using ALU and MBR.

If the instruction is one which writes to memory, for example a 'store contents of register A in addressed memory location', the sequence would be:

$$[IR]_{address} \rightarrow MAR$$
$$\text{field}$$

$$[A] \rightarrow \quad MBR$$
$$[MBR] \rightarrow \quad M$$

In all the examples in this chapter it is assumed that the action described symbolically as

$$[IR]_{address} \rightarrow MAR$$
$$\text{field}$$

involves taking account of the basic addressing mechanism in use on a particular computer, such as base and displacement addressing or base and current page addressing, as described in Section 5.4.

Some instructions both read from and write to memory during their execution. Consider, for example, the 'increment and skip if zero' instruction. The effect of this instruction is to take the contents of some memory location, increment its value by 1 and if its value is now zero skip the next instruction in sequence; otherwise execute the next instruction in sequence. Symbolically this is

(a) $[IR]_{address} \rightarrow \quad MAR$
    field

(b) $[M] \rightarrow \quad MBR$

(c) $[MBR] + 1 \rightarrow MBR$

(d) $[MBR] \rightarrow \quad M$

(e) If $[MBR] = 0$ then $[PC] + 1 \rightarrow PC$.

Having read the value of the data from memory in step (b), step (c) increments this value and at step (d) it is written back to memory at the same address, since the contents of the MAR has not been altered. The skip if zero part of the instruction is carried out in step (e). It must be remembered that the PC has already been incremented during the fetch phase to point to the next instruction in sequence; so the only modification necessary is to increment it by a further one if the incremented value which is still stored in the MBR is now equal to zero.

6.2.3 *Branching instructions*

Branch instructions are a particular subset of memory reference instructions that reference memory for the purpose of transferring control rather than doing some arithmetic or logic.

Consider an unconditional branch instruction. The required effect is to transfer control to the address defined in the branch instruction. The instruction which will be executed after the current one is pointed to by the contents of the PC register. This is incremented by one during the fetch phase of every instruction on the assumption that the next instruction to be executed is going to be the next one in sequence. In the case of a branch instruction, however, the address of the next instruction to be executed is contained in the branch instruction, and so all that is necessary is for this address to be transferred to the PC. Consequently, the execute phase for an unconditional branch instruction can be represented symbolically as

$$[IR]_{address \atop field} \rightarrow PC$$

If the branch is a conditional branch, all that is necessary is for the condition to be examined to decide whether to transfer the address field of the IR to the PC or not, as illustrated by the 'increment and skip if zero' instruction considered in Section 6.2.2.

6.2.4 *Indirect and indexed addressing*

If indirect addressing is specified for any instruction (see Section 5.3.2), this will introduce an additional memory read into the sequence of actions.

For example, consider again an instruction to fetch some data from memory and perform some arithmetic or logic function on this data, where the address is defined as being indirect. The sequence would be

$$[IR]_{address \atop field} \rightarrow MAR$$
$$[M] \rightarrow MBR$$
$$[MBR] \rightarrow MAR$$
$$[M] \rightarrow MBR$$

Perform appropriate action using ALU.

So far as the CPU is concerned, the main effect of indirect addressing is to slow down the execution of an instruction by requiring an additional memory read cycle.

If indexed addressing is specified, there is the additional step of adding the contents of the index register to the address defined in the instruction before the memory access can be made. For the same instruction as just described, but using indexing rather than indirect addressing the sequence would be

$$[IR]_{\text{address field}} \rightarrow MAR$$

$$[MAR] + \begin{bmatrix} \text{index} \\ \text{register} \end{bmatrix} \rightarrow MAR$$

$$[M] \rightarrow MBR$$

Perform appropriate action using ALU.

For both indirect and indexed addressing there is also the additional requirement of identifying whether these addressing techniques are being used or whether direct addressing is specified. Consequently the sequence of actions described above may well require a series of steps which entail testing whether one of the above addressing techniques is specified or not, and conditionally branching to the appropriate sequence of steps.

6.3 Architectural considerations

This chapter has so far discussed features of a CPU that are normally found on most computers. From the user's point of view what makes computer systems differ from each other is essentially the instruction set provided. From a performance point of view, in addition to the facilities provided by the instruction set it is important to look at how the basic components are structured and interconnected. These are the factors that determine how a computer will perform. It is in this area that the term 'architecture' can be sensibly applied. The word is directly analogous to the more familiar meaning of architecture applied to buildings. All buildings are constructed from the same basic components: bricks, cement, glass, door frames, etc. What makes buildings quite different from each other, both visually and functionally, is the way in which these components are put together, and the overall design is the work of an architect. All computers can be said to be constructed from the same basic components (memory, registers, ALU, etc.) but they are functionally different because of the way in which they have been structured and interconnected by the computer architect.

In this section we will consider ways of arranging for the basic components of the CPU to be controlled and connected.

6.3.1 *Synchronous and asynchronous processors*

Section 6.2 examined the sequence of steps that the CPU must perform in order to fetch and execute an instruction. Certain of these steps must wait until the previous step is complete before commencing. For example, during the fetch phase the instruction cannot be moved from the MBR to the IR until a previous step ([M] $\rightarrow$ MBR) has completed, which is dependent on the time for completion of a memory read. This is not necessarily true for all steps, however. The program counter PC, for example, can be incremented at any stage during the fetch/execute cycle, after its value has been transferred to the MAR. Since incrementing it is an operation purely internal to the CPU and involves the PC and perhaps the ALU, it takes less time to complete than a memory transfer operation. Since nothing else can proceed until the memory transfer, transferring the instruction from memory to the MBR, is complete, the incrementing of the PC can be done concurrently with this memory transfer. This is the reason why the PC is incremented for all instructions even though for some, such as a branch instruction, it is not really necessary because they are going to alter the value of the PC during execution.

The total time required to execute an instruction depends on the instruction itself. The fetch phase is the same for all instructions, but the execute cycle may require either one or a number of steps. Also the time for each step in the fetch/execute cycle is not necessarily the same. As has just been indicated, the time for a memory transfer will be relatively large compared to the time for an operation on an internal register. Also, operations involving simple register transfers, such as those which would occur in executing a branch instruction, will take less time than those operations on registers requiring arithmetic or logic to be performed. The timing for each of the steps can be achieved in one of two ways.

A *synchronous* processor has an internal processor *clock*. This is an electronic circuit that generates electronic pulses at regular and accurate intervals of time, and is usually based on a crystal controlled oscillator for accuracy and stability. Each step must commence operation on a clock pulse and although each transfer step always requires the same amount of time each time it is performed, some steps may require more than one clock period (the time between consecutive pulses) to complete whereas other steps will require less than one clock period to complete.

This leads to a relatively simple processor construction, but has the disadvantage that since not all steps need the same amount of time, some operations can not commence until the next clock pulse, even though the preceding step is complete.

An *asynchronous* processor is one where initiation of the next step takes place immediately the previous step is completed. This will remove any idling of the processor as it waits for the next clock pulse and consequently should result in an increase in speed of the processor. However, this is tempered by the fact that extra logic circuitry is required to detect the end of each event. Not only does this extra logic make an asynchronous processor more expensive (the cost of the logic circuits to detect the end of a step will usually be greater than that for a simple clock), but the fact that the end of an event has to be detected will take some time, and reduce the time saved over a synchronous processor.

Asynchronous operation of the CPU is, however, generally faster but more complex and costly than synchronous operation because more hardware is required.

6.3.2 *Interconnection methods*

The central processing unit is made up of a number of component parts, which were described in Section 6.1. These component parts can be interconnected in several ways. The way the components are connected can have a significant effect on the machine instructions that can be provided and on the speed of operation of the CPU; consequently it is one of the architectural features that can distinguish one machine from

If you examine the individual information transfer steps that make up machine instructions, as described in Section 6.2, then for a simple CPU, with just one user register known as the accumulator, some of the transfer paths are shown in Fig. 6.2.

In this example, there is a requirement for four address transfer paths and six instruction and operand transfer paths, a total of ten paths. Obviously the more registers there are available and the more machine instructions that are to be provided, the more information transfer paths will be required.

These transfer paths can be implemented in one of three ways, either using a point-to-point connection, a common bus or a multiple bus system.

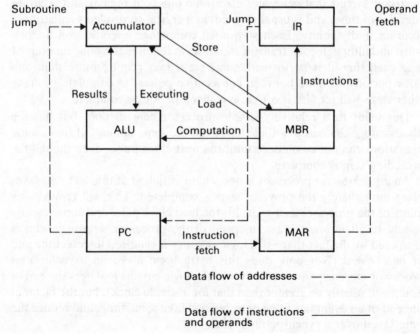

Fig. 6.2

If a computer is to achieve a reasonable speed of operation, it must be organized in a parallel fashion. This means that in order for a component to handle a full word of data at a time, the data transfer between components must be done in parallel (all the bits of a word are transferred simultaneously) which implies that a considerable number of wires (lines) are needed for the necessary connection. Such a collection of wires which have some common identity is called a *bus*.

In the case of a *point-to-point* bus system, every information transfer path required is provided by a dedicated bus. In the simple example shown in Fig. 6.2, each data flow path would be implemented as an individual bus. The advantage of such a system is that many transfers could be taking place simultaneously, thereby tending to lead to a fast CPU. The disadvantage is that it would be very expensive to provide all the buses. On studying the transfers that are necessary for the operation of a machine instruction, it can be seen that a lot of the transfers can not logically take place simultaneously even though physically it is possible. Consequently a full point-to-point bus system for internal CPU organization is almost never used.

At the other extreme there could be a *common bus* system. Implemented with a common bus system, the simple CPU whose data flow paths are shown in Fig. 6.2 would be as shown in Fig. 6.3.

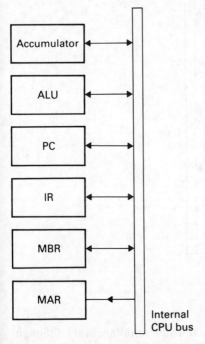

Fig. 6.3

All data transfers take place along this common bus. To enable information to be transferred from one register to another, there need to be some logic gates (on/off switches) which enable only the required registers to be actively connected to the bus at the appropriate time. The advantage of the common bus system is that it is very inexpensive, but the disadvantage is that only one transfer can take place at once. There is therefore no possibility of concurrent operations and consequently this type of computer can be slow.

The most usual form of internal CPU bus system found on many machines is the *multiple bus* system, which is a compromise between the two extremes just described. Here there is more than one bus to which a number of components are attached, sometimes with some registers connected by a point-to-point bus if necessary. Often the data flow requirements are implemented with two buses, an address bus and a data bus. For the machine described in Fig. 6.2, implemented as a multibus machine the structure might be as in Fig. 6.4.

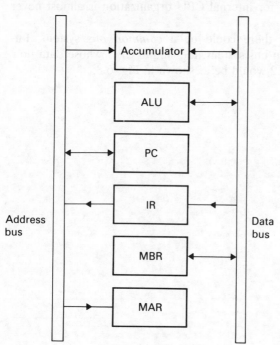

Fig. 6.4

This system would allow more than one transfer simultaneously although allowing only one transfer on each bus at any time.

6.4 Control unit

To execute instructions, the CPU must have some means of generating the appropriate control signal to initiate the next step in the correct sequence, as discussed in Section 6.2. The various ways that have been developed fall into one of two categories.

- hardwired control
- microprogrammed control.

6.4.1 *Hardwired control*

Consider the sequence of steps involved in the fetch/execute cycle as defined in Section 6.2. Each step will require a time period, defined by the clock if the processor is a synchronous one. The particular action at each step is defined by the state of

(a) The output of the decoder—this defines the machine instruction to be executed.
(b) The clock, relative to the time period at the start of this machine instruction.
(c) Any test flags set in the ALU (see Section 6.1.2).

The particular operation carried out by the CPU is controlled by a complex logic circuit known as an *encoder*. This, as illustrated in Fig. 6.5, has as input a series of lines from the decoder, the clock and the ALU test flags.

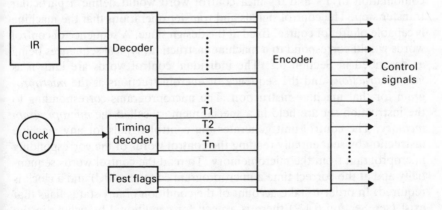

Fig. 6.5

Only one line from the decoder will have a signal on it indicating which particular instruction is to be executed, and only one line from the clock will have a signal on it indicating which step period is the current one (the signal reverting back to line T_1 at the end of execution of this instruction). Only those lines from test flags set will have signals on them. Each output line corresponds to a particular control signal, a combination of which will result in one of the transfer steps that the CPU is capable of performing. As was indicated in Section 6.3.2, all registers are connected to a bus system to allow information to pass between appropriate registers. Connections to the bus system are through *gates*. A gate is normally *inhibited* (this means that there is no connection to the bus), but can be *enabled* by the application of a control signal. Thus to transfer information from one register to another the output gate of one register and the input gate of the other register would both need to be enabled, requiring two control signals. According to the combination of input lines to the encoder with signals on them, only the appropriate output lines will generate control signals which cause that particular step to be performed.

6.4.2 *Microprogrammed control*

An alternative way of generating the appropriate control signal at the appropriate time is by a software technique known as microprogrammed control.

Consider a control word whose individual bits represent the various control signals in Fig. 6.5. Within the control word a one bit would indicate the presence of a control signal, a zero the absence of that control signal, there being as many bits as control signals. This is, in fact, a simplification of a realistic system, but it is useful for illustrating the concept. A particular combination of 1's and 0's in a control word would define a particular transfer step. The control signals and transfer operations that the machine is capable of are, of course, fixed at the design stage. A sequence of control words would correspond to a machine instruction, typical sequences being as described in Section 6.2. The individual control words are known as *microinstructions* and the sequence of microinstructions as the *microprogram* for that machine instruction. The microprograms corresponding to the instruction set are held in a special memory called the *microprogram memory*. The control unit generates the control signals for any machine instruction by sequentially reading the control words of the corresponding microprogram from the micromemory. To read the control words sequentially and at the correct time a microprogram counter (μPC) and a clock is required. In order to take account of the condition of any status flags that exist (see Section 6.1.2) there is a need for conditional branching in the microprogram.

Not all microprogrammed computers allow the user to write his own microprograms. Sometimes the microprograms, which are supplied by the manufacturer, are stored in ROM and cannot be altered. On other computers, for example the Hewlett Packard HP21MX, the microprogram memory can be altered, and consequently the user can define his own microprograms for machine instructions. These computers are said to be user microprogrammable.

The following points are important:

(1) Microprograms define the instruction set of the computer. If the microprogram memory can be written to, then the instruction set is not irrevocably fixed but can be changed by altering or adding microprograms. This can offer flexibility to the designer and user of the computer.

(2) Hardwired control units are inevitably faster than microprogrammed ones because there is dedicated circuitry for the control functions.

(3) Since execution of a machine instruction involves a number of fetches from the microprogram memory, the speed of this memory plays a vital role in determining the overall speed of the computer. Consequently the microprogram memory is usually implemented in a small, very fast dedicated memory rather than the main memory.

6.5 Summary

The architecture of a CPU is decided by

- The control functions that it is capable of initiating and consequently the instruction set that can be provided;
- The method of interconnection of component parts; and
- The availability of a hardware floating point unit.

Inevitably the design of a particular CPU is a compromise between cost and speed. The faster components and transfer methods tend to be more expensive, and so the designer has to have a clear idea of the requirements for the machine in order to make it process information quickly at a reasonable cost. However, the speed of hardware continues to increase, and its cost decrease, and consequently the difference in speed between hard wired control units and microprogrammed control units is becoming less significant. Consequently the flexibility provided by microprogrammed control is becoming more significant. Other techniques for central processor unit design are discussed in Chapter 10.

6.6 Problems

6.1 Explain and comment upon the effect of each of the following micro-instructions, what is their total effect and what can you deduce about the memory of the computer? (You can assume that the computer is a two address asynchronous computer with the following registers which are referred to by the mnemonics given.)

Register	Mnemonic	
Memory buffer register	MBR	
Memory address register	MAR	
Program counter	PC	
Instruction register	IR	
Accumulator	ACC	
First operand address	OP1	} within instruction register
Second operand address	OP2	

Micro-instruction sequence

Pulse	Micro-instruction
1	Read memory
2	PC = PC + 1
3	Transfer MBR to IR
4	Transfer OP1 to MAR
5	Read memory
6	—
7	Transfer MBR to ACC
8	If ACC = 0 transfer OP2 to PC
9	Transfer PC to MAR
10	End

6.2 (a) What is a micro-instruction?

(b) How does the implementation of micro-instructions allow a manufacturer to build a range of computers each with the same set of machine instructions but with different processor speeds?

(c) A two address computer contains the following registers:

A an accumulator
IR the instruction register containing the fields
f the function code
i the index bit
OP1 the first operand address
OP2 the second operand address
MAR the memory address register
MBR the memory buffer register
PC the program counter
I an index register

Describe, with reasons, the effects of each of the following micro-instructions and the effect of the sequence as a whole.

Transfer PC to MAR

Read memory
Increment PC by 1
Transfer MBR to IR
Decode for f
Transfer OP1 to MAR
Read memory
Add I to MBR giving A
If A = 0 then PC = OP2
    else decrement I by 1

How could the complete machine instruction be used and what other machine instruction, if any, would be required to make this instruction function in the way you have described?

6.3 The CPU of a two address byte computer contains the registers defined in Problem 6.1 and 16 general purpose registers R0, . . ., R15.

Define the sequence of micro-instructions needed to implement the fetch and execute phase of each of the following two instructions:

    BALR R1, R15 (PC + 2 → R1, branch to address in register 15)

and

    A R1, THREE   (add contents of location THREE to register 1)

6.4 Write the sequence of micro-instructions required to implement each of the following three instructions:

(a) Add the number N to register A
(b) Add the contents of memory location N to register A
(c) Add the contents of the memory location whose address is in memory location N to register A

Assume that each instruction consists of two words. The first word specifies the operation and the addressing mode, and the second word contains the number N.

6.5 Consider the store instruction described in Section 6.2.2, 'store contents of register A in addressed memory location'. Assume the CPU is driven by a continuously running clock, such that each transfer step is 200 ns in duration. How long will the CPU have to wait in each of the two memory access steps assuming that a read or write operation takes 0.9 μs to complete? Also estimate the average percentage of time that the CPU is idle.

7 Interrupts

During the execution of a program by a computer, many situations can arise which require prompt attention, either to utilize the whole computer system efficiently or to prevent a serious mishap occurring. In order to ensure that such situations are dealt with as quickly as necessary, the execution of the current program is interrupted. The computer is then able to execute a program which determines the cause of the interrupt and deals with it accordingly. After this interruption has been dealt with, the original program can be resumed at the point of interruption, unless a computer error or programming error caused the interrupt.

This chapter will describe the interrupt system and how it operates. Not only will it describe ways of handling a single interrupt but it will also describe techniques for dealing with the situations of either multiple interrupts occurring simultaneously or interrupts occurring before a previous interrupt has been fully dealt with.

7.1 Causes of interrupts

This section examines several situations which could require the processor to be interrupted. They are not in any order of priority, since the priorities are not the same for every computer system. The question of priorities is dealt with in Section 7.4.

7.1.1 *Hardware fault*

The hardware circuitry carries out various checks for its own malfunction. Two examples are power failure and memory parity.

The electricity needed to operate a computer is usually supplied by the national or local power company via its existing power distribution system. In the event of a mains power failure, processing must be suspended. It is desirable that when supplies are resumed, processing can continue from where it was suspended. Because of the volatile nature of registers and of some main memory systems (see Chapter 4) an orderly shutdown procedure is required; otherwise data can be lost, erroneous information can be written into the memory and other malfunctions can occur during the fraction of a second that power is being lost. To guard against such an occurrence, the voltage supplied to the computer is monitored continuously. If it drops to, say, 85 per cent of its nominal value, the assumption is that a power failure is occurring and an interrupt request is generated. If this power fail interrupt is serviced immediately (it will have to be assigned the highest priority as described in Section 7.4) there will be sufficient time for the computer to save the contents of all its registers and shut itself down. When power is restored the contents of the registers can be reloaded (either by the operator or sometimes automatically) and operation resumes from where it was interrupted. If the main memory is non volatile, the registers can be stored in special memory locations reserved for this. In the case of a volatile main memory, the situation is more difficult. Back-up battery supplies are often used, switched on by the power fail detector. This will stop corruption of the data for hours, particularly as, with processing halted, it is not being accessed.

For detecting memory errors a parity bit is provided for every word in the memory. If on a memory access, either a read or a write, one of the bits of a stored word is written into or read from incorrectly then the word transferred will not have the correct parity. In this case, an interrupt is generated.

The action on receipt of this interrupt could be to try the memory transfer again a number of times. If this is successful, processing can continue from where it was interrupted. Alternatively, if it is not successful the original program cannot be continued because either incorrect data would be used in a calculation, or an instruction which differs from that intended by the programmer would be executed.

7.1.2 *Program errors*

There are a number of errors that can be committed by a program, as a result of an error situation introduced by the programmer.

Errors which occur while using the arithmetic and logic unit often generate an interrupt. An overflow error is one such condition. Usually an overflow occurs because the programmer did not anticipate that a computed result would exceed the range of the machine. On receipt of this interrupt the action would be either to terminate execution of the program or to transfer control to a user-supplied subroutine which might allow processing to continue despite the overflow condition.

Another condition is that of memory protection violation. It is possible for a program to generate an address which is outside the range of that program. Some areas of memory should be protected, such as the operating system routines used by many programs. Obviously a program must be prevented from overwriting such an area of memory. A memory block is protected by the supervisory programs executing a special PRO-

TECT MEMORY instruction and can be unprotected by execution of an UNPROTECT MEMORY instruction. These instructions are *privileged* instructions which mean that only the supervisory programs can execute them. If a user program tries to write to an address which is in a protected part of main memory, an interrupt will be generated. On receipt of this interrupt the action is usually to terminate execution of the program and generate an appropriate error message.

Attempts can be made by a program to perform operations on data that is not compatible with the way the data is stored. An example would be to interpret the contents of a word as a series of characters when in fact the bit pattern within the word does not correspond to characters in the character code being used. It is also possible to branch to a word, to continue execution from that point on, when the word branched to does not contain a valid instruction operation code. All of these are examples of conditions which could generate an interrupt to indicate that something is wrong.

7.1.3 *Real time conditions*

Computers are often used for the monitoring and control of real time processes. These are processes in which the computer is expected to respond to some situation in a realistic time scale (often very quickly).

In medicine, for example, a computer may be used to monitor a patient's heart beat. If there is a significant reduction in the frequency or power of the heart beat an interrupt can be generated which enables the computer to take immediate action such as the triggering of alarm bells.

A potentially costly real time situation can occur during the control of a machine tool by a computer. If an expensive part is being machined and the cutter breaks, both the part and the machine may be damaged. By detecting that tool breakage has occurred immediately and putting the equipment on to standby, consequent damage to the part and the machine can be prevented.

7.1.4 *Input/output*

Even though most peripheral devices seem to the user to operate at very high speed they actually operate very slowly compared with the rate at which the CPU operates (see Chapter 8). The slower peripheral devices such as card readers, paper tape readers, printers, and typewriter terminals, transfer characters one at a time. In order to be able to make use of the CPU during the time the peripheral is transferring the character it is necessary that the peripheral device is able to interrupt the CPU on completion of the transfer. The CPU can then initiate the transfer of the next character. In the case of faster peripheral devices, such as magnetic disk, a block of characters can be transferred, and an interrupt only takes place on completion of the block transfer (see Chapter 8).

Consequently the interrupt facility is very important as an aid to maximizing the use of the CPU during input/output.

7.2 Interrupt handling

Suppose the CPU is running a program when it receives a request from, say, a peripheral to interrupt its processing and deal with the peripheral. This will involve transferring control to a second program which will deal with the peripheral. This second program is often called an *interrupt service routine*. On completion of the interrupt service routine, control will have to transfer back to the original program, at the point at which it was interrupted, in order for it to continue. There must, therefore, be a mechanism to allow for error free switching between the program that is being executed when an interrupt occurs, and another program to deal with the interrupt, and back again.

Since the main purpose of an interrupt system is to utilize the CPU to the full, it is obviously important that the response to an interrupt is very quick. Since it is totally unreasonable to expect every user program to include an instruction to test the state of some interrupt flag after every instruction, in case something requires attention, it follows that the interrupt mechanism must be automatic and provided by the CPU. However, as we shall see, there may be a case for using software to assist the hardware in the provision of the interrupt mechanism.

The problem of transferring control from a program to an interrupt service routine, while remembering the position in the interrupted program so that a return can be made, is essentially the same problem as that faced when writing a subroutine (see Section 5.2.3). However, as we have just seen, the transfer of control from the interrupted program to the interrupt service routine must be performed by the hardware automatically on receipt of an interrupt and not as a result of the CPU executing an instruction. On completion of the interrupt routine, control has to be given back to the interrupted program, and this can be done by software in just the same way as with a subroutine.

In addition to the requirement that the response must be quick, it is also important that it is error free, so that the program is not corrupted. The condition of the CPU must be exactly the same on return from the interrupt service routine as it was before the interrupt occurred.

7.2.1 *The state of the CPU*

In order for the CPU to be in the same state after an interrupt has been serviced as it was before, it is necessary to be able to preserve the state of all the components of the CPU when the interrupt occurs. The CPU consists essentially of a series of registers and lines containing control signals (see Chapter 6). To preserve the registers will require the execution of some instructions to store the contents of the registers in some area of main memory. However, since the actions required to preserve the control signals would destroy them, the signals cannot be preserved. The solution lies in the fact that in the brief instant between completing the execute phase of one instruction and the fetch phase of another instruction, the CPU control signals are always in the same state, regardless of which instructions have been executed. Consequently, when an interrupt occurs the CPU finishes executing the current instruction *before* it accepts the interrupt. It is then merely necessary for the interrupt service routine to store the appropriate registers immediately it is given control and to reset the registers back to these values immediately before giving control back to the original program.

7.2.2 A simple interrupt system

In order to see what is required of the hardware when an interrupt occurs, consider in more detail the situation of the CPU executing a program, the only other program involved being the interrupt service routine. We will also assume that there can only be one reason for the interrupt, and that a further interrupt cannot occur while this one is being dealt with. Although this is a false situation, it enables a clear picture to be seen of the actions to be taken on receipt of an interrupt. The other complications are dealt with later. Figure 7.1 shows the program in memory and the point at which an interrupt occurs.

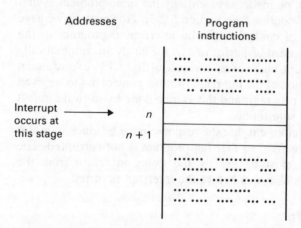

Fig. 7.1

Assume that an interrupt occurs while the CPU is executing the instruction stored at the memory location with address n. The PC register will, of course, contain the address of the next instruction to be executed, namely $n + 1$. In order for control to be given to the interrupt service routine, the address of that routine must be transferred into the PC so that the next instruction fetched is the first one of the interrupt service routine. This unfortunately would destroy the address $(n + 1)$ already in there, and so the contents of the PC will have to be preserved (by the hardware) in a particular memory location. Also, it is possible that we may wish to hold the interrupt service routine in any part of memory that is convenient and so the address of the start of it must also be stored in a special memory location. These two memory locations are often at 'one end' of memory, say at locations 0 and 1. This results in the situation where the hardware always uses fixed addresses, but the service routine can be placed anywhere in main memory. To recap: when an interrupt occurs, the following events will take place:

(a) The CPU will complete execution of the current instruction;
(b) The hardware will
   (1) Transfer the contents of the PC register to memory location 0.
   (2) Transfer the contents of memory location 1 to the PC;
(c) The CPU will continue by fetching the
   instruction whose address is in the PC,
   i.e., the first instruction of the interrupt service routine.

The first instructions in the interrupt service routine will be to store all the general registers in some memory locations. In fact, it is only necessary for it to store away those registers that it is making use of during its processing.

Just before the interrupt service routine is finished, the last instructions will be to restore the general registers from the memory locations used for their preservation. Finally, control can be transferred back to the original program by executing a branch instruction which will 'branch indirect through memory location 0'. This will cause the contents of location 0 $(n + 1)$ to be put into the PC register, and processing will continue from where it was interrupted.

7.3 *Identification of interrupt source*

To explain the fundamental ideas of dealing with an interrupt, the previous section was restricted to situations where there was only one reason for the interrupt. The mechanism for handling interrupts must now be extended to deal with a number of interrupt causes. Section 7.1 described some of the possible causes of interrupts, and since it is reasonable to assume that the action required on receipt of an interrupt will be dependent on the cause of that interrupt, it follows that there need to be a number of interrupt service routines, one for each cause of an interrupt. Consequently it is necessary to identify the precise cause of the interrupt.

One way this can be done is to have *multiple interrupt lines*. Each type of interrupt will generate an interrupt signal on its appropriate interrupt line. Each line has associated with it its own pair of main memory locations, one of which contains the address of the service routine as described in Section 7.2.2. However, there are some circumstances which require more than one type of interrupt on one line. If an interrupt from a particular peripheral device, for example, is considered to be a unique interrupt source then it could have its own interrupt line. But this would mean that the design of the CPU hardware fixes precisely the peripheral devices that can be attached to it. Obviously this reduces the ease with which different peripheral devices can be attached to the same CPU. Consequently, particularly in respect of input–output, it is usual to have a number of devices (interrupt sources) all attached to the same interrupt line. When an interrupt signal occurs on such an interrupt line, the particular device requesting the interrupt has to be identified. This can be achieved either by a software technique or implemented as a hardware function.

Because of the potential delay in responding to an interrupt (either because the interrupt is not responded to until completion of execution of the current instruction or because it has to wait its turn as described in Section 7.4), an interrupt line actually consists of two lines. One is the *interrupt request* line, this being the line which will transmit the interrupt request signal to the CPU. The other line is an *interrupt acknowledge* line. When the CPU is ready to accept the interrupt it will send an interrupt acknowledge signal so that the interrupt request signal can be turned off by the source of the interrupt.

7.3.1 *Identification by software*

When a device signals an interrupt request, the hardware causes control to transfer to a service routine as described in Section 7.2.2. In that section it was assumed that this would be the device service routine. If, however, there can be a number of devices attached to this line, the routine will be an interrupt service routine whose task is to identify the device requesting the interrupt and then to transfer control to its device service routine. In order to determine which device is requesting the interrupt, the routine will examine all the devices on that line, one at a time. This is known as *software polling*. A common technique is to make use of a special skip instruction which allows examination of a particular peripheral device interface (see Chapter 8). On a peripheral device interface there is often a flag bit which is set to one when an interrupt request is generated and back to zero when the interrupt has been dealt with. One of the set of input–output instructions examines this flag and skips the next instruction when it is set to 0. An example of a software polling interrupt service routine is shown below. It assumes that four devices are attached to the same interrupt request line, that memory location 0 is used to store the PC and that the address of the interrupt routine is stored in location 1.

Address	Contents	Comment
0		location for saving PC
1	500	start address of interrupt routine
2	1575	start address of service routine for device 1
3	1625	start address of service routine for device 2
4	1650	start address of service routine for device 3
5	1715	start address of service routine for device 4
.		
.		
.		
500	SKDEV 1	skip next instruction if device 1 is not requesting interrupt.
501	BR 2 (indirect)	indirect jump to location 1575 (device 1 requesting interrupt).
502	SKDEV 2	
503	BR 3 (indirect)	
.		
.		
506	SKDEV 4	
507	BR 5 (indirect)	
.		
.		
1575		start of service routine for device 1.
.		
.		
1624	BR 0 (indirect)	return to original program being executed before interrupt occurred.
1625		start of service routine for device 2, etc.

7.3.2 *Identification by hardware*

The above solution to the problem of identifying the source of the interrupt is relatively cheap to implement but slow in operation because of the time taken to execute the instructions, particularly in the case of the device that is polled last. However, in the days when hardware was expensive, this was an acceptable solution. Since hardware costs are now relatively low, many interrupt systems use a hardware identification system.

This hardware system is called *vectored interrupts*. In general, this name refers to all interrupt handling techniques that allow the interrupting device to identify itself to the CPU by supplying a special code or address to the CPU.

When the CPU is ready to accept an interrupt, it sends an interrupt acknowledge signal. Of the devices attached to that interrupt line, only the device requesting the interrupt will respond. It does so by sending to the CPU an address. This address could be the start address of the service routine for that particular device. However, this would impose the restriction that the interrupt service routine for a given device always starts at the same location. An improvement would be for the address that is sent to the CPU by the device to be that of a word in memory in which the PC can be saved, the following word containing the start address of the service routine. Each device would have associated with it a unique pair of main memory locations.

The following, then, is the sequence of events:

(a) A device generates an interrupt request signal
(b) The CPU completes execution of the current instruction and then sends an interrupt acknowledge signal.
(c) The device requesting the interrupt will send to the CPU (usually via the I–O data bus as described in Chapter 8) an address of a location in memory, and then turn off the interrupt request signal.
(d) The CPU hardware stores the current value of the PC in this memory address and loads the contents of the next word in store into the PC and commences processing again. The instruction now being executed is the first instruction of the device service routine.

The name 'vectored interrupts' stems from the idea that the specification to the CPU of a unique memory location for that device causes a specific directed change in processing sequence.

In contrast to the software polling method, the process is very quick, requiring not much longer than the two memory cycles required for the main memory accesses. Also the time taken to enter a particular device service routine is independent of the number of devices attached to that interrupt line. The disadvantage is that it requires more specialized hardware, in particular in the peripheral interface.

7.4 Priority systems

Section 7.3 extended the mechanism for handling interrupts to allow for a number of interrupt sources, by looking at methods for identifying the source of the interrupt. This section will extend the mechanism even further by examining the situation in which an interrupt occurs before the previous one has been fully serviced, or when multiple interrupts occur simultaneously. Although the chance of more than one interrupt occurring at precisely the same instant is not very high, it must be remembered that an interrupt is not accepted until the machine instruction being executed when the interrupt occurs is complete. During this brief delay there may have been a number of interrupts generated, all of which require *servicing simultaneously*. Consequently the often used term of interrupts 'occurring' simultaneously in fact refers to interrupts requiring 'servicing' simultaneously. In this latter case the interrupt handling system is faced with the decision of which interrupt to service first. In the other case, that of interrupts occurring before a previous one has been fully serviced, the mechanism must decide whether to finish the servicing of the interrupt it has already started, or whether to leave off and accept and service the new interrupt request. Obviously there needs to be some system of priorities in order to resolve these questions.

7.4.1 *Nested interrupts*

There are many occasions when an interrupt occurs while a previous one is being serviced. If, as discussed later, it is necessary to process this second interrupt immediately, the processing of the first interrupt will have to be suspended. We have already seen (Section 7.2.2) that when an interrupt is accepted the address of the instruction that would have been executed next is stored away so that control can be transferred back to it after the interrupt has been serviced. If a second interrupt occurs that must be dealt with immediately, it is important that the address that is now stored away (the address of the next instruction in the first interrupt service routine) is *not* stored at the same location as the first address that has been stored away (the address of the next instruction in the original program). Otherwise control would not be able to return to the original program. Therefore these addresses must be stored in separate locations. This ability to allow interrupts to interrupt previous interrupt service routines safely is called *nested interrupts*. This is why, in the vectored interrupt system described in Section 7.3.2, *each* device has associated with it a unique pair of main memory locations.

If the computer has a stack facility (see Section 5.5), the return address can simply be PUSHed on to the stack. This is discussed more fully in Section 7.5. Each time an interrupt is accepted the PC will be pushed on to the stack. They will, of course, be POPed off the stack in the reverse order, this being the order in which the interrupt servicing will now be completed.

So long as the stack is sufficiently large, interrupt routines can be nested to any depth.

7.4.2 *Enabling and disabling interrupts*

There are a number of occasions when it is necessary temporarily to prevent an interrupt occurring. Consequently there needs to be provision for disabling the interrupt mechanism and also, therefore, provision for enabling interrupts so that they may continue to occur.

There are essentially three levels of interrupt disable:

(a) Disabling of interrupts from a particular peripheral device. Usually this can be achieved by the inclusion of an interrupt inhibit bit on the device interface.

(b) Disabling of interrupts from sources of lower or equal priority. When there is a system of priorities given to the various interrupt sources, it must be possible to delay an interrupt that comes from a source of equal or lower priority than that currently being serviced. In some computers, this selective inhibiting of interrupts can be achieved by setting the appropriate bits in an interrupt mask register (see Section 7.4.5).

(c) Disabling of all interrupts from any source. This can be achieved in two ways. The first is a temporary inhibit imposed by the hardware, so that on acknowledging an interrupt the CPU will execute at least one instruction before allowing further interrupts. This ensures that the first instruction in the interrupt service routine is executed. If there is a need for more instructions in the service routine to be executed without interruption, the first instruction must be an interrupt disable instruction. This is, in fact, the other way of disabling interrupts. An interrupt disable instruction is usually provided, which, when executed causes the CPU to ignore all interrupts until a specific instruction is executed to enable interrupts. An example of the use of this can be seen by considering again the software polling system explained in Section 7.3.1. The device requesting the interrupt is not acknowledged until it is addressed by the CPU. Since a device requesting an interrupt is not always on top of the polling list, a number of instructions in the interrupt service routine need to be executed before this device is addressed. Unless interrupts are disabled during this period, the device will continue to interrupt the CPU, causing the system to repeatedly re-enter the interrupt service routine.

7.4.3 *Software allocation of priorities*

If the recognition of the interrupt source is achieved by a software polling routine (see Section 7.3.1), the priority is inherent in the order in which devices are examined or polled. If two devices interrupt simultaneously, the first one that is examined is the one accepted first. Even for interrupts that do not occur simultaneously it is interesting to note that the one that interrupts first may not be accepted first. If, after having switched to the interrupt service routine because of a device interrupt, an interrupt from another device occurs, and the second device is polled before the original one, then the second interrupt is accepted first.

Because the priority system is determined by the polling order, the priorities can be easily changed by rewriting the interrupt service routine to poll in a different order. Also it is possible for a device with a very high priority to be polled more often than other devices.

7.4.4 *Hardware allocation of priorities*

There are two basic methods of allocating priority by hardware.

The first method is concerned with the priority amongst devices attached to the same interrupt request line. Instead of the interrupt acknowledge line being a common line to which all devices are attached in parallel, the interrupt acknowledge line passes from one device to the next in turn. A signal from the CPU on the interrupt acknowledge line will only be passed to the next device if the current device is not requesting an interrupt as in Fig. 7.2.

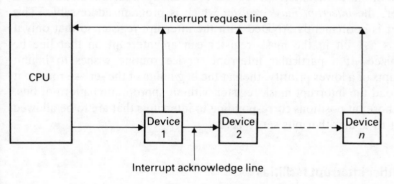

Fig. 7.2

This technique, known as *daisy chaining*, has its priority system built into the order in which the devices are attached to the interrupt acknowledge line, those closest to the CPU having the highest priority.

The second method of providing a priority system by hardware lies in the ability to have multiple interrupt lines. Each interrupt source is allocated to one particular interrupt line (there could be a number of interrupt sources attached to the same line). Priority between lines can be achieved simply by a priority arbitration circuit to which all lines are attached. If simultaneous interrupt request signals occur this circuit will send the acknowledge signal to the line with the highest priority. The allocation of priority is sometimes fixed and sometimes programmable. If there is only one interrupt source to each interrupt line, total priority between sources is achieved. In practice, it is usual to have a number of interrupt sources (for example, peripheral devices) attached to each line. Priority between lines can be achieved by the arbitration circuit just described, and priority between devices on each line can be achieved by daisy chaining the interrupt acknowledge line between the devices. In this multi-level interrupt system, device recognition is usually achieved by vectoring.

7.4.5 *Interrupt masking*

The advantage of a software priority system is that it can be modified at any time merely by polling in a different order. In contrast, however, the faster hardware system is fixed by the wiring of the circuits. In order to combine flexibility with speed, a combined software/hardware system has been developed called *interrupt masking*. Here, all interrupt lines attached to the CPU are associated with a bit position in an *interrupt register*. If an interrupt on a line is generated, it will only be recognized by the CPU if the corresponding bit in the interrupt register is a 1. In order to allow the pattern of bits in the interrupt register to be changed there is an associated register, the *interrupt mask register* which is program addressable. This register is permanently ANDed with the interrupt register so that only if there is a 1 bit in the mask register can an interrupt on that line be recognized. If a particular interrupt service routine wishes to inhibit interrupts of a lower priority, then at the beginning of the service routine it must load the interrupt mask register with an appropriate pattern of bits. Only those bit positions corresponding to interrupts that are to be allowed are set to 1, all other bits set to zero.

7.5 Other interrupt facilities

We have seen how it is necessary for the contents of the PC and any general purpose registers being used to be saved at the commencement of dealing with an interrupt, in order to allow control to return to the interrupted program. Stacks can be used for this purpose just as they can in subroutine handling (see Section 5.5.3). The CPU can push the PC on to the stack and the service routine can PUSH all the general registers on to the stack at the start of the service routine. On completion of the service routine, these values can be POPed off the stack. If interrupts are nested, the stack mechanism will ensure that the values are retrieved from the stack in the correct order (see Section 7.4.1). However, there is still the requirement for a dedicated memory location to keep the address of the interrupt service routine.

We have seen the need to keep the address of the interrupt service routine in a dedicated memory location so that on acceptance of an interrupt the CPU can load this address into the PC and then recommence execution by fetching what will be the first instruction of the service routine (see Section 7.2.2). An alternative to this is to place an *instruction* in the dedicated memory location. The CPU then merely needs to transfer the contents of this location to the IR and then to continue. This instruction would usually be a branch instruction which would cause control to transfer to the first instruction of the interrupt service routine.

7.6 Examples of real interrupt systems

Having gradually developed the requirements for an interrupt system and seen various alternative ways of implementing such systems, it will be interesting to look briefly at the interrupt handling mechanisms actually used on some existing computers. The examples chosen are from a large main frame computer, a minicomputer and a microprocessor, although it is important to note that these examples are not necessarily typical of each class of computer. In particular, many microprocessors have more sophisticated mechanisms than the one described here. It is left as an interesting exercise for the reader to investigate the interrupt handling mechanism of the computer to which access is available.

7.6.1 *The interrupt mechanism of the IBM 370 series of machines*

On an IBM 370 computer, the program that is currently being executed (regardless of whether it is a user program or a supervisor program) is described by a double word data item that is a register in the CPU, called the Program Status Word (PSW). Amongst many other things (the length of the PSW is 64 bits) the PSW holds the address of the next instruction to be executed; in other words it incorporates the PC.

There are six interrupt lines, each line having associated with it a pair of storage locations, one being a place to store the CURRENT PSW, the other containing a NEW PSW, the PC field of which contains the address of the interrupt service routine.

When an interrupt occurs, the CPU performs the following actions:

(a) The current PSW is stored in the appropriate store location, called the OLD PSW;

(b) The current PSW is replaced by a new PSW which is held at another store location;

(c) The CPU continues processing according to the new current PSW.

Clearly the new PSW should be set up to describe a program that will deal with the interrupt, that is the interrupt service routine. After this routine has serviced the interrupt, it replaces the current PSW by the old PSW and the interrupted program is resumed.

Each interrupt line is associated with an interrupt type. The six types are:

Restart	an interrupt caused by depression of the restart key on the operator's console.
External	caused by a signal from outside, such as an external clock or timer, or a line attached to another computer.
Supervisor call	caused by execution of an SVC instruction. This allows a user's program to enter the operating system.
Program	a user program error condition (Section 7.1.2).
Machine check	detection of machine malfunction (Section 7.1.1).
Input/output	an input or output interrupt. Note that input/output is primarily performed by a channel (see Chapter 8). The CPU is only interrupted on completion of transfer. Since there is only one I/O line the interrupt service routine must first determine which I/O device is interrupting by examining information stored in memory by the channel. Then it can call the appropriate device service routine.

In the case of interrupted interrupts, suppose an interrupt of the *same* type has occurred. In order to prevent the old PSW being replaced by the current PSW (thereby ensuring that control could not revert to the original interrupted routine) the interrupt of the same type is masked out by a field in the PSW which indicates whether or not an interrupt of a certain type can occur or not. (If interrupts are inhibited they are queued until they can be accepted.)

Priority is assigned by the hardware to the processing of the interrupt lines in the following order.

High priority	1	Machine check
	2	I/O
	3	External
	4	Program
	5	SVC
Low priority	6	Restart

7.6.2 *The interrupt mechanism of the Hewlett Packard HP21MX*

The vectored priority interrupt system has up to 60 distinct interrupt levels, each of which has a unique priority assignment. Each interrupt level is associated with a numerically corresponding interrupt location in memory. Of the 60 interrupt levels, the two highest priority levels are reserved for hardware faults (power fail and parity error), the next two are reserved for block data transfer channels and the remaining levels are available for I/O device channels.

As an example, an interrupt request from I/O channel 12 will cause an interrupt to memory location 12. This request for service will be granted on a priority basis higher than afforded to channel 13 but lower than that afforded to channel 11. Thus, a transfer in progress via channel 13 would be suspended to allow channel 12 to proceed. On the other hand, a transfer in progress via channel 11 cannot be interrupted by channel 12.

Any device can be selectively enabled or disabled under program control, thus switching the device into or out of the interrupt structure. In addition, the entire interrupt system, except power fail or parity error interrupts, can be enabled or disabled under program control using a single instruction.

It is assumed that when control is transferred to the corresponding memory location on receipt of an interrupt, this location contains a branch to subroutine instruction which will transfer control to the service routine. The hardware will also store the return address (the contents of the PC) in the first word of the service routine. The storage of all registers is the responsibility of the service routine.

7.6.3 *The interrupt mechanism of the Motorola M6800 microprocessor*

There is only one interrupt request line for I/O which all interrupting devices share. There is no hardware priority system. When the CPU recognizes an interrupt request, it stacks the contents of all the CPU registers. It then causes a switch to a program whose start address is in a fixed memory location. This program must, of course, be a device polling service routine.

Interrupts from individual devices can be inhibited by software, and when an interrupt is accepted the hardware automatically inhibits interrupts so that the polling routine is not interrupted. A device service routine can, however, enable the interrupt system, so allowing itself to be interrupted if required.

7.7 Summary

This chapter has presented the need for and means of achieving an interrupt system. In many computer applications it is necessary to be able to interrupt the normal execution of programs in order to service higher priority requests that need urgent attention. Most computers, large and small, have a mechanism for dealing with such situations, although the complexity and sophistication of interrupt handling schemes vary from computer to computer.

However, as the cost of hardware continues to decrease there is a move to hardware implementations rather than slower software facilities.

7.8 Problems

7.1 Investigate the interrupt handling mechanism of a computer to which you have access.

7.2 (a) Explain what you understand by:

  (1) an interrupt, suggesting reasons for the cause of an interrupt
  (2) interrupt vector and interrupt service routine.

 (b) Explain the sequence of events when the following interrupts occur, assuming,

  (1) the second and third interrupts occur before the servicing time of the first interrupt has elapsed.
  (2) an interrupt with priority value 1 has the lowest priority.

  The sequence of interrupts is:

Interrupt Number	Time of Occurrence	Priority
1	t_1	1
2	t_2	2
3	t_2	3

7.3 An interrupt handling routine usually masks out interrupts of the type that it is handling. If, however, an interrupt of type A occurs, followed by an interrupt of type B, followed by another interrupt of type A it is necessary to ensure that this second type A interrupt does not wipe out information on the first type A interrupt. Using the priority structure given in Section 7.6.1 determine which interrupt handling routines should allow which other interrupts. What special provision would you make for machine-check interrupts?

7.4 On a machine using base registers, it is necessary for the interrupt handling routines to save one base register for use by the interrupt routine itself. However, the instruction to store a base register itself requires the use of a base register to address the word where the base register is to be stored. Because an interrupt can occur at any time, the values of all the base registers are unknown at the start of the interrupt handling routine which means it has no base register available to use for the store base register instruction. Devise a solution to this problem, and if you are using a base register computer, check to see the manufacturer's solution.

7.5 Explain why the nesting of interrupts is desirable and what the necessary requirements are of a system which allows nesting of interrupts. Explain two ways of achieving these requirements.

7.6 A 16-bit minicomputer has a multilevel interrupt system with twenty levels. Describe how the interrupt priorities of peripheral devices can be resolved by hardware to give each device a unique priority. If the system is vectored, explain how control can be passed to the interrupt service routine of the highest priority interrupt.

7.7 Assume a machine with a vectored interrupt system, and a stack on which CPU registers can be stored. Describe the sequence of events from the time a device requests an interrupt, until execution of the interrupt service routine is started. If machine instructions require one to four memory cycles to execute, estimate the maximum number of memory cycles that may occur before execution of the interrupt service routine is started.

8 Data transfers

The architecture of a computing machine will now be discussed in relation to the ways in which it communicates with the outside world. One of the basic features of a computing machine is its ability to send and receive data to and from other devices. These range from slow peripheral devices which transfer one character at a time, for example a teletype device, to very fast devices which require a whole block of data to be transferred, such as a magnetic disk device or even another computer if the machines are part of a distributed network. Also, the devices may be very close to the computer, in which case connection can be by a simple cable (multiconductor cable if information is transferred in parallel), or they may be some considerable distance away, in which case the provision of multiconductor cables becomes too expensive.

This chapter will look at the above features as they relate to software, e.g., input/output as it affects the programmer, and to some of the hardware aspects of peripheral and 'line' transfers. The software aspects of input/output are introduced initially in our discussion of the simpler methods which apply directly to many micro and minicomputers (Sections 8.1 to 8.3) through to the more sophisticated techniques used on larger mainframe computers (Section 8.4). On the hardware side, transferring data over lines is important not only in dealing with input/output along an I/O bus or channel but also in connection with the distribution of processing and data over a network as we shall see in Chapter 9.

8.1 Input/output bus and the input/output interface

Since a number of peripheral devices are usually connected to a computer, there has to be some means by which only one of these devices can be selected to perform some input or output task. This can be achieved through the use of an input/output bus—the I/O bus. In some respects, the I/O bus is similar to the internal CPU bus system described in Chapter 6. Connected to the wires which form the bus are registers in the peripheral device interface. However, unlike registers in the CPU which are completely under the control of the CPU, the peripheral devices act in an autonomous way. The CPU initiates their actions, but does not subsequently have any control over their operation.

A bus, to which I/O devices are connected, consists of three sets of lines, used for the transmission of address, data and control signals. When the CPU wishes to send data to a particular I/O device it places a unique identity code, or address, on to the address line. Only the device that recognizes that code will respond to the command that is placed on the control line. Figure 8.1 shows a typical structure of a computer system with a single I/O bus. In many so called 'single bus systems', the I/O and memory share a common bus. In such a system, each register on each interface can be identified uniquely by allocating it a specific memory address, and transfers of information to or from a register on an interface can be achieved by any of the appropriate instructions in the instruction set, rather than by a limited number of specific I/O instructions.

In a system such as that illustrated in Fig. 8.1, reading data from a peripheral device and storing it in memory is a three stage process (output being the reverse).

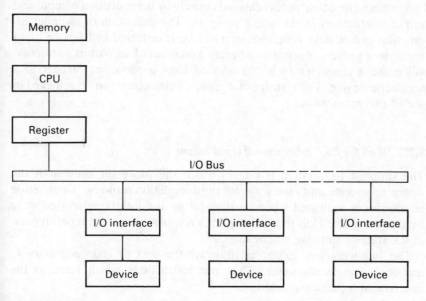

Fig. 8.1

(a) Device → I/O interface
(b) I/O interface → register
(c) Register → memory

A device is attached, by cable, to an I/O interface. The interface is plugged into one of a number of I/O slots, each of which is assigned a fixed address.

The interface is the communication link. It includes three basic elements:

(a) A control bit—this is a one bit register (flip flop) which when turned on generates a start command to the device to start its I/O.
(b) A flag bit—this is set on by the device when transmission between the device and its interface is complete. It can be tested or cleared under program control.
(c) A buffer register—this is the register in which the data that has been read, or which is to be written, is stored.

When a start command is generated, *one* character is transferred between the interface buffer register and the device or vice versa.

8.2 Programmed input/output

Programmed input/output is achieved entirely by the execution of input and output instructions in the user's program. The execution of an input instruction causes data (one character) to be transferred in from an input device to a processor register, whereas execution of an output instruction will cause a character to be transferred from a processor register to a peripheral device. The transfer of a group of characters can be achieved in one of two main ways.

8.2.1 *'Wait for flag' programmed input/output*

The simplest I/O system is one in which the processor commands the device to operate and then waits for the completion response. Completion of transfer is indicated when the flag bit on the interface referred to in Section 8.1 is set. Thus the 'waiting' for a response is in fact a repetitive test of the state of this flag bit, by the CPU.

The following two examples illustrate the sort of code necessary to transfer a single character. They use instructions which refer to the interface at a particular address.

Input	STC	12	Set control bit on I/O interface 12 to 1 to start transfer of a character;
	SFS	12	Skip next instruction if flag bit is set, indicating transfer complete;
	JMP	*-1	Branch to instruction in previous word;
	LIA	12	Load contents of interface buffer register into accumulator.

Output	OTA	15	Transfer contents of accumulator to buffer register on interface 15;
	STC	15	Set control bit to start transfer of a character;
	SFS	15	Skip next instruction if flag bit is set, indicating transfer is complete;
	JMP	*-1	Branch to instruction in previous word.

The test and loop instructions cause the processor to test repeatedly the state of the flag bit until it is set to 1, indicating that the transfer is complete. To transfer a group of characters would require a further loop around the above code, since the examples given only transfer one character.

Although this method of achieving input/output is very simple to program, the disadvantage of it is one of slowness. It might not be obvious at first why it is necessary to test repeatedly the flag bit to see if the character has been transferred. Obviously it is important to ensure that one character has been transferred before attempting to transfer the next, but why does the program have to loop, apparently 'waiting' for this to occur? To answer this, consider the following example of the timing of the character transfer process. Suppose the computer is reading data from a fast paper tape reader at 1000 characters per second. Further, assume a memory cycle time of one microsecond and that consequently the following input code takes, say, 10 microseconds from the time a character is available (i.e., the LIA instruction is executed) until the next character needs to be transferred (i.e., the next time it arrives at the STC instruction).

loop	STC	12	
	SFS	12	
	JMP	*-1	
	LIA	12	
	STA	Memory address	(store the contents of the accumulator in the addressed memory location)
	JMP	Loop	(this would actually have to be a conditional branch, depending on whether the end of the tape had been reached or not).

The paper tape reader reading at a speed of 1000 characters per second will transfer one character in 1000 microseconds. Consequently, after every 1000 microseconds, the CPU is to take 10 microseconds to deal with the character obtained and then wait another 1000 microseconds for the next character to arrive.

Not only does this explain why an idle loop is necessary (because the peripheral device is so very slow compared to the speed of the processor) but it also illustrates the disadvantage of this method of input/output. In the above example, the CPU is only usefully active for 10 microseconds in every 1000. That is, it is only being used for about 1 per cent of the time and 99 per cent of the time it is idling, waiting for the character to be transferred.

8.2.2 *Interrupt programmed input/output*

This method makes use of an interrupt facility (see Chapter 7). It removes the time spent testing the status of the flag bit of the interface by allowing the input/output transfer of data to be initiated by program instruction and allowing the hardware to cause an interrupt when the transfer is complete. In this case, the interrupt service routine would perform the task of transferring the character between the interface buffer register and the processor register (an accumulator for example) and would then initiate the transfer of the next character. While the character is being transferred the processor is free to be used for other tasks, with the provision that it will be interrupted when the next character has been transferred.

The following example shows an interrupt routine for reading 80 characters from an input peripheral device. The mainline program has to set up the address of the interrupt service routine, initialize a count of the number of characters to be transferred and initiate the transfer of the first character. While the character is being transferred the processor can continue with another task. On the completion of each character transfer, the interrupt service routine is entered which initiates the transfer of the next character. The program runs as follows.

Main program
Set up address of interrupt service routine

	STC	14	Set control bit to start the transfer of the 1st character.
	—		
	—		
	—		
	—		
	—		
charcount	DEC	−80	The number of characters to be transferred.

Interrupt service routine

LIA	14	Transfer character from interface buffer to A register.
STA	Memory location	Store this character in memory
INC	Charcount	Increment the character count
BZ	END	All characters are transferred if charcount = 0
STC	14	Initiate transfer of next character
B	RETURN	Return to interrupted program

END	BSUB	SUB	Branch to subroutine to process characters
RETURN	B	0 (indirect)	Return to interrupted program.

On completion of the transfer of all 80 characters it is assumed that some processing of the characters is necessary and so control is transferred to a subroutine, SUB, to do the required processing.

8.3 Autonomous input/output—DMA

Programmed input/output (particularly interrupt driven) is fine for transferring relatively few characters to or from relatively slow peripheral devices. If, however, there are a large number of characters to be transferred, the CPU will be spending a large portion of its time just dealing with the individual characters, since each character still passes through the CPU and its MAR and MBR on its way to the memory. Also, some of the faster peripherals, such as magnetic tapes or disks, may be able to transfer characters at such a rate that there would not be time to process the interrupt service routine for one character before the next character had arrived. Consequently there is a need for some sort of system for allowing a peripheral device to transfer characters directly to memory, without going 'through' the CPU. Such a facility is known as *Direct memory access* (DMA). This is achieved by incorporating many of the functions which are performed by software in a programmed I/O method into a hardwired controller.

This controller will need

(a) a register for generating the memory address

   (b) a register for keeping track of the word count

   (c) a register to store the command received from the CPU specifying the function to be performed.

   (d) a register to be used as a data buffer between the peripheral device and the main memory.

Since DMA is used for connecting high speed devices it must be remembered that with the devices such as magnetic tapes and disks there is no need to convert information to and from character format. Consequently the usual unit of transference is a word.

On a single bus computer where the memory bus and I/O bus are in fact the same bus, a peripheral device is connected to the bus by the DMA controller rather than by an interface.

On a computer with a separate I/O bus, however, the DMA controller will need to be connected directly to the memory, bypassing the CPU. Figure 8.2 illustrates such a connection. It is still necessary for the CPU to be connected to the DMA in order for control signals to be sent to the DMA controller to initiate the data transfers.

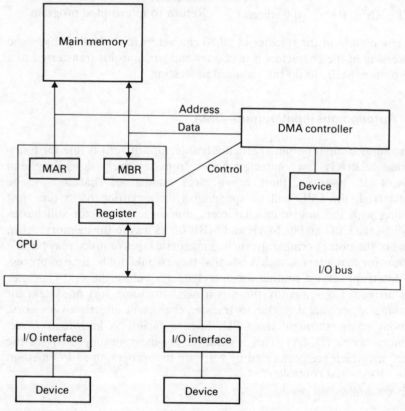

Fig. 8.2

To start an I/O operation using the DMA it is necessary for the program to do the following:

(a) load the initial memory address
(b) load the count of the number of words to be transferred
(c) load a control word defining input or output
(d) execute a START command.

On receiving the START command the DMA will proceed with the data transfer independently of the CPU, so enabling the CPU to continue processing another part of the same program or another program altogether. There is, however, the possibility of a conflict when both the CPU and the DMA controller wish to access memory at precisely the same time. Because the transfer of data from very fast peripheral devices attached to the DMA cannot be held up, priority is usually given to the DMA in preference to the CPU. In most cases the CPU will originate the majority of memory access cycles, and hence in the case of contention the DMA can be thought of as stealing a cycle from the CPU. Hence this is often known as 'cycle stealing'. It must be remembered, however, that in any program not all the instructions are memory reference instructions, and so, although all instructions involve a memory access to fetch them, only a proportion will access memory during execution. Consequently cycle stealing will only take place occasionally, although it is not possible to predict the effect of the DMA facility on the execution time of an instruction and it therefore follows that the execution time of a program will be unpredictable.

8.4 Input/output channels

The two methods of input/ouput described, programmed I/O and DMA, are adequate for the requirements of most micro and minicomputers. DMA is usually associated with high speed peripheral devices, whereas programmed I/O is used with low speed devices. With large mainframe computers, however, the size of the system and the cost of the CPU make it desirable to get the maximum use out of the CPU. Consequently it seems reasonable that all input/output operations should be provided through a DMA facility rather than have the slow CPU consuming programmed I/O. Since it would be uneconomic for each peripheral device to have its own DMA controller, particularly when not all peripherals will be involved in data transfers simultaneously, it seems reasonable that the DMA facility should be shared between a number of peripheral devices. The concept of a small processor acting as a shared DMA facility to a number of peripheral devices is known as a *channel*. Strictly speaking, the term channel was introduced by IBM on their 360/370 range of computers and has since come into common use, although in fact not all computer manufacturers use the term 'channel' to describe their equipment of a similar type. On most large mainframe computer systems, all communication with external devices is through one or more channels, there being three basic types of channel:

(1) Selector channel
(2) Multiplexer channel
(3) Block multiplexer channel.

An example of a system configuration is shown in Fig. 8.3.

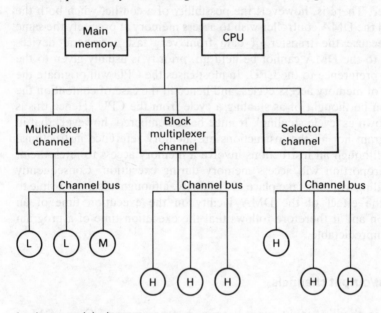

L = low speed device

M = medium speed device

H = high speed device

Fig. 8.3

8.4.1 *Selector channels*

The selector channel provides an exclusive input/output path for a single high speed peripheral device. There may be a number of devices attached to the selector channel but at any time it is totally dedicated to the selected device and, until released, cannot be used for another input/output function. It is used to transfer a block of words to or from memory and provides the necessary synchronization between the speed of transfer of words from the device and the speed of transfer of words to or from main memory. Additionally it performs parity checking or parity insertion. It generates a 'transfer complete' interrupt on completion of the block transfer, or an error interrupt on detection of bad parity or on receipt of an error signal from the device.

8.4.2 *Multiplexer channel*

A multiplexer channel is used for connecting a number of slow and medium speed devices. Since the rate of transfer of data over the channel to the memory is very much greater than the rate at which a device can supply data to the channel, a multiplexer channel is able to operate with a number of peripheral devices simultaneously. It is, in fact, able to operate in either one of two modes. The channel can be totally dedicated to one medium speed device for a burst transfer, in which case it acts like a medium speed selector channel. In the multiplex mode the channel will poll around the devices connected to it and transfer the next character or word from each device in turn that is ready for a transfer. Parameters relating to the operation of each of these devices, such as character count and memory data address, are usually kept in fixed locations in the main memory. When the channel is attached to a specific device, it fetches the appropriate parameters from memory and on disconnection the updated values are placed back at the same location.

8.4.3 *Block multiplexer channel*

The block multiplexer channel combines the best features of both the selector and multiplexer channels. It operates in a very similar way to that of a high speed multiplexer channel operating in burst mode. Like a selector channel it is used to transfer a block of data at very high speed. Like a multiplexer channel, it is able to poll round the devices attached to it to transfer blocks of data in turn as required. The advantage over a selector channel can be seen if the operation of transferring data from a magnetic disk file is considered. To retrieve data from a disk file the following operations are necessary

(1) Seek for the appropriate track
(2) Search that track for the appropriate record
(3) Read the data from that record.

The first two operations will involve a considerable delay in the mechanical movement of the disk heads and if a selector channel is being used it will tie up the entire channel during the whole of the above operations. With a block multiplexer channel, after the appropriate commands have been sent to the device, the channel can be released to allow it to service other devices and be reconnected when the device is ready to transfer the block of data.

8.4.4 *Channel programming*

As described earlier, a channel is a small processor that is responsible for carrying out input/output to and from all the peripheral devices attached to it. To examine the operation of a channel in a little more detail, let us consider the sequence of events that takes place during an I/O operation on an IBM 370 computer. The following description is not complete (for the details refer to the appropriate IBM manual) but it illustrates the concepts, and although it relates to a specific range of machines, similar events take place on equipment from other manufacturers.

To start a transfer between a device and main store the following must be specified:

(1) The channel address
(2) The device address (there will be more than one device attached to a channel)
(3) The operation to be performed, e.g., input or output
(4) The number of bytes to be transferred
(5) The main storage address of the area from which or to which the transfer is to proceed.

On the 370 these are specified as follows. The supervisor initiates a transfer by executing an SIO (Start IO) instruction, which has the following layout.

SIO	OP Code		Base register	Displacement
	0 7	16	20	31

The sum of the displacement and the contents of the base register is formed as usual but it does not refer to a main storage location. Instead the resulting 32 bit number is treated as a channel address and a device address as follows:

	Channel address	Device address
0 15	16 24	31

The remainder of the information is specified as follows. Location 48_{16} in main store is used specially as a *channel address word* (CAW). When an SIO is executed the CAW must contain the address of a *channel command word* (CCW) set up somewhere in main store. A channel command word is actually a double word with the following format:

Command	Data address
0 7 8	31

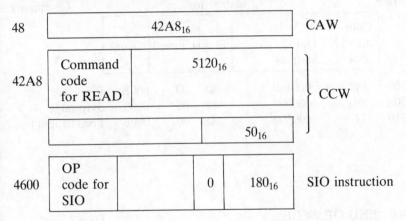

CCW	Chaining flag		Count	
	32	37	48	63

As an example, suppose that a user program issues an **INPUT** command referring to a card reader which is connected on channel 1 and has address 80_{16}. Suppose that the user program buffer is at address 5120_{16} and that 80 bytes of information is to be input from each card.

The supervisor has to:

(1) set up a CCW (say at address 42A8)
(2) set up the CAW (at address 48_{16})
(3) execute an SIO instruction (say at 4600_{16})

The contents of the various words are as follows:

Note that immediately the SIO instruction is executed by the CPU the channel starts carrying out the I/O transfer independently of the CPU. The channel and the CPU operate autonomously. Finally the channel interrupts the CPU when the I/O transfer is complete.

Further, once the SIO instruction has been executed the CAW can be utilized by the CPU to initiate transfers through other channels. The similarity between the CPU and a channel becomes clearer when channel programming is considered. Consider the situation where it is necessary to perform a definite sequence of I/O operations, one immediately after another. For example, suppose that when a job fails the operating system

(1) Prints a message on the line printer
(2) Ejects a page
(3) Prints a message at the top of the next page.

If this was achieved by the operating system executing three SIO instructions, it would also be burdened with the task of handling the interrupt that occurs at the end of each. It is possible for this to be achieved by a sequence of CCWs, executed by the channel in sequence. This sequence of CCWs is known as a channel program. Referring back to the layout of the CCW it can be seen that bits 32–37 contain a chaining flag. This is essentially a bit pattern indicating whether this is the last CCW in a sequence or whether the next pair of words in store contain a CCW to be executed next by the channel.

A channel, once initiated by the CPU, obeys the commands until either it has completed all of the operations, or an error condition arises. It then interrupts the CPU.

For the above example, the channel program would be a sequence of three CCWs as follows:

Location	Instruction					Comments
	Command code	Data address	Flag	Unused	Count	
000300	01	000400	40	00	000B	Print line
000308	88	000000	40	00	0000	Skip page
000310	11	000500	00	00	000F	Print header line
—						
—						
—						
—						
000400	'END OF PAGE'					Data
—						
—						
000500	'TOP OF NEW PAGE'					Data

8.5 Front end processors

The task of dealing with input/output becomes even more involved in a system which provides interactive facilities to users via a large number of terminal devices attached to the CPU. The following characteristics are typical of many such systems.

(1) A large number of terminal devices (perhaps 150 to 200);
(2) The terminals may be of different speeds—perhaps low speed printing devices and high speed visual display units;

(3) The different types of terminals may have different communication protocols (see Chapter 9);

(4) There may need to be character translations to be performed;

(5) Every character received has to be echoed back to the terminal immediately so as to appear instantaneous;

(6) Characters from a terminal are collected together in a buffer assigned to that terminal, so that there is a large number of data buffers.

One of the main objectives in an interactive system is to achieve fast response to individual users. The more time that the CPU is involved in doing all of the above tasks the less time there is for it to be doing the required tasks.

Under these circumstances the concept of input/output being achieved through a channel, where a channel was a simple processor sharing the main memory with the main CPU, can be extended to the point where the channel does in fact become a processor comparable in sophistication to a CPU. That is, all the tasks relating to gathering input from terminals and routing results back to terminals are performed on a computer, this computer being linked to the main CPU and main memory in the same way that a channel is. The computer that is used in this way is said to be a 'front end processor'. It is really a logical extension of the ideas of a channel, designed to take many of the tedious tasks associated with input/output off the main CPU so that it can concentrate on the required tasks. The main CPU has only to deal with one interrupt, that of the block transfer, instead of with individual interrupts from the terminals.

8.6 Introduction to line transfers

The previous part of this chapter has essentially dealt with the software aspects of input/output. It has presented a developing sophistication of input/output methods to cater for the different requirements of small and large computer systems. Regardless of where the data is being transferred to or whether the CPU is to be interrupted after every character or every block of characters, it is necessary to consider just how data is to be transmitted along a line, whether the line is physically short, for peripheral devices in the immediate vicinity of the CPU, or long, for devices situated at remote locations. The remainder of this chapter will present an overview of the concepts involved in the transmission of data.

8.7 Transmission codes

The transmission of data consists essentially of passing a stream of binary digits over a line connecting two devices. The information is transmitted as a sequence of characters, each character being in a particular code.

8.7.1 *The Baudot Code*

A very common code used in telegraphy and telex transmissions (the public system for sending telegrams and telex messages) is the *Baudot Code* (see Fig. 8.4). It is a five bit code and consequently it would appear that only 32 different characters can be represented. In order to get round this restriction there are two special characters called letter shift and figure shift which correspond to an upper and lower case form. After a letter shift character is received all the following characters are from the letter shift alphabet until a figure shift character is received, and vice versa. The main disadvantage with the Baudot Code is that there is still a very limited

1	2	3	4	5	Lower case	Upper case
•	•				A	–
•			•	•	B	?
	•	•	•		C	:
•			•		D	who are you?
•					E	3
•		•	•		F	
	•		•	•	G	
		•		•	H	
	•	•			I	8
•	•		•		J	Bell
•	•	•	•		K	(
•				•	L	)
		•	•	•	M	.
		•	•		N	,
		•	•		O	9
•	•			•	P	0
•	•	•		•	Q	1
•		•			R	4
•		•			S	!
				•	T	5
•	•	•			U	7
	•	•	•	•	V	=
•	•			•	W	2
•		•	•	•	X	/
•		•		•	Y	6
•				•	Z	+
					Blank	
•	•	•	•	•	Letters shift	↓
•	•		•	•	Figures shift	↑
		•			Space	
			•		Carriage return	<
	•				Line feed	≡

Fig. 8.4 The Baudot code

character set and that there is an apparent lack of logic in the allocation of bit combinations to each character.

8.7.2 *Binary coded decimal (BCD)*

If the data to be transmitted consists of numbers only it may be convenient to transmit these in their binary form rather than convert to one of the other more extensive codes. BCD is a system of coding in which each decimal digit is converted into its binary form and the whole number is then transmitted as a sequence of binary coded decimal digits. To represent any one of the decimal digits 0,1, . . ., 9 requires four bits. For example, the decimal number

6 8 4 1

would be coded as

0110   1000   0100   0001

8.7.3 *The EBCDIC Code*

One of the major general codes in use is the *EBCDIC Code*. This stands for Extended Binary Coded Decimal Interchange Code. Each character is represented by an 8 bit number and the complete code is given in Fig. 8.5. This code was initially developed by IBM for use on their 360/370 range of computers but has since been used on a number of other computers.

8.7.4 *The ASCII Code*

In an attempt to counter the threat of a proliferation of codes the American Standards Association (now known as the American National Standards Institute) defined a 7 bit code known as ASCII—the American Standard Code for Information Interchange (Fig. 8.6). This code has been widely accepted and is now in general use. It is often made into an 8 bit code by the addition of a parity bit. This involves the addition of the 8th bit such that the sum of binary 1's in any character is an odd number (odd parity) or an even number (even parity), both systems being in common use. This parity can be used as a crude check that the correct bits have been transmitted.

A number of characters in the ASCII code have special meanings. They are used as special control characters in connection with serial synchronous transmission (see Section 8.9.4). The meanings of some of the control characters in Fig. 8.6 are as follows:

SOH (start of heading)   Used to indicate the start of control information at the beginning of a block of data.

Most significant digits

Least significant digits	0000	0001	0010	0011	0100	0101	0110	0111	1000	1001	1010	1011	1100	1101	1110	1111
0000	NULL				SP	&	-									0
0001									a	j			A	J		1
0010									b	k	s		B	K	S	2
0011									c	l	t		C	L	T	3
0100	PF	RES	BYP	PN					d	m	u		D	M	U	4
0101	HT	NL	LF	RS					e	n	v		E	N	V	5
0110	LC	BS	EOB	UC					f	o	w		F	O	W	6
0111	DEL	IL	PRE	EOT					g	p	x		G	P	X	7
1000									h	q	y		H	Q	Y	8
1001									i	r	z		I	R	Z	9
1010			SM		¢	!		:								
1011					.	$	,	#								
1100					<	*	%	@								
1101					(	)	_	'								
1110					+	;	>	=								
1111					|	¬	?	"								

NULL	Null/Idle	PRE	Prefix
PF	Punch off	SM	Set mode
HT	Horizontal tab	PN	Punch on
LC	Lower case	RS	Reader stop
DEL	Delete	UC	Upper case
RES	Restore	EOT	End of transmission
NL	New line	SP	Space
BS	Backspace		
IL	Idle		
BYP	Bypass		
LF	Line feed		
EOB	End of block		

Fig. 8.5 The EBCDIC Code

	Most significant digits							
	000	001	010	011	100	101	110	111
0000	NULL	DC0	♭	0	@	P		p
0001	SOM	DC1	!	1	A	Q	a	q
0010	EOA	DC2	"	2	B	R	b	r
0011	EOM	DC3	#	3	C	S	c	s
0100	EOT	DC4	$	4	D	T	d	t
0101	WRU	ERR	%	5	E	U	e	u
0110	RU	SYNC	&	6	F	V	f	v
0111	BELL	LEM	'	7	G	W	g	w
1000	BKSP	S0	(	8	H	X	h	x
1001	HT	S1	)	9	I	Y	i	y
1010	LF	S2	*	:	J	Z	j	z
1011	VT	S3	+	;	K	[	k	{
1100	FF	S4	,	<	L	\	l	|
1101	CR	S5	−	=	M	]	m	}
1110	SO	S6	.	>	N	↑	n	ESC
1111	SI	S7	/	?	O	←	o	DEL

(left margin label: Least significant digits)

NULL	Null/Idle	BKSP	Backspace	DC0–DC4	Device control
SOM	Start of message	HT	Horizontal tab	ERR	Error
EOA	End of address	LF	Line feed	SYNC	Synchronous idle
EOM	End of message	VT	Vertical tab	LEM	Logical end of media
EOT	End of transmission	FF	Form feed	So–S7	Separator information
WRU	'Who are you?'	CR	Carriage return	♭	Blank
RU	'Are you . . .?'	SO	Shift out	ESC	Escape
BELL	Audible signal	SI	Shift in	DEL	Delete/Idle

The ASCII Code

Fig. 8.6

STX (start of text)	Indicates the end of the heading and the beginning of a block of data.
EXT (end of text)	Used to indicate the end of a message text which started with an STX.
EOT (end of transmission)	Signifies the end of a transmission.
ENQ (enquiry)	Used to request a response, such as the address or status of the receiver.
ACK (acknowledge)	Positive acknowledgement usually indicating a successful reception.
BEL (bell)	Character used to activate a visible, audible alarm at the receiving terminal device.
NAK (negative acknowledgement)	Indicates unsuccessful reception.

SYN (Synchronous Idle)	Used to identify a sequence of synchronizing bits.
ETB (end of transmission block)	Used to indicate the end of a physical block of data where this may not coincide with the logical format of the data being transmitted.
CAN (cancel)	Used to signify that all preceding data in the block or message should be ignored.

8.8 Modulation

As has already been discussed, the transmission of data consists essentially of passing a stream of binary digits over a line connecting two devices. In many cases, particularly when the connection is remote, the line that is used is a normal telephone line simply because such lines already exist and are very extensive. Telephone lines are designed to carry an analogue signal, and the easiest analogue signal to place on a line is a regular alternating current which may be represented by the sine wave in Fig. 8.7.

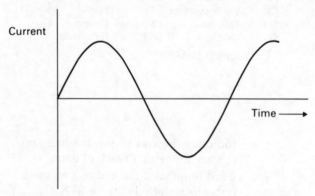

Fig. 8.7

Such a waveform has three characteristics

(1) Frequency or pitch
(2) Amplitude or loudness
(3) Phase or timing.

Each of these attributes may be altered in some way to indicate a 0 bit or a 1 bit of the signal that is to be transmitted.

The modification of the signal is known as *modulation*. If the frequency of the signal is altered this is known as frequency modulation. If the amplitude is altered, it is known as amplitude modulation, and if the phase is altered it is known as phase modulation.

Figure 8.8 shows the effect that each of these modulations would have on the normal carrier signal for a binary signal of alternating 0's and 1's.

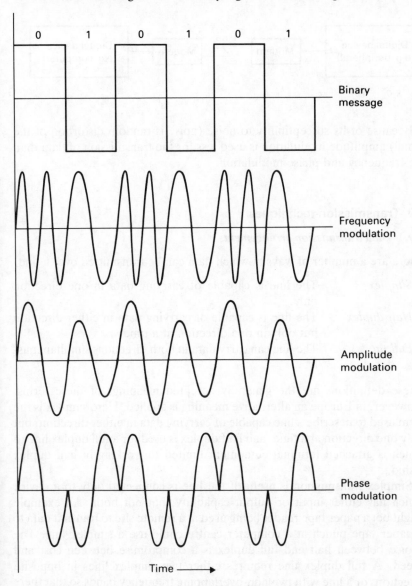

Fig. 8.8

Signals emitted from a peripheral device have to be *modulated* before they can be sent over a telephone line. At the other end *demodulation* has to take place so that they can enter the computer back in a binary form. The conversion is effected at each end of the line by a device known as a *modem* (MODulator—dEModulator). Transmission will therefore take place between the modems as in Fig. 8.9.

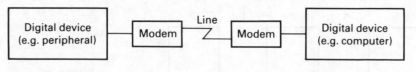

Fig. 8.9

Because of its susceptibility to noise (noise is random distortion of the signal) amplitude modulation is used less for the transmission of data than are frequency and phase modulation.

8.9 Transmission techniques

8.9.1 *Data transmission arrangements*

There are a number of ways in which data can be transmitted over a line.

Simplex   The line is capable of carrying data in one direction only.

Half duplex   The line is capable of carrying data in either direction but only in one direction at a time.

Full duplex   The line can carry data in both directions simultaneously.

These definitions are the generally accepted meanings of these terms. However, in Europe an alternative meaning is applied. Here simplex is the term used to describe a line capable of carrying data in either direction, but only one direction at a time, and half duplex is used for a full duplex line to which is attached terminal equipment limited to working in half duplex fashion.

Simplex transmission is useful if the line is connected only to a device which has either input or output capability, but not both. An example might be: a paper tape reader being used at a remote site to transmit data to a paper tape punch at a computer centre could use a simplex line. The choice between half and full duplex is a compromise between cost and speed. A full duplex line requires either two simplex lines in opposite directions or a line with two non-overlapping frequency bands so that there are two independent transmission facilities, one in each direction. Half duplex requires the same sort of transmission line as simplex, but with switches at both ends to connect either the transmitter or the receiver, but not both, to the line.

Consequently full duplex transmission is usually more expensive to provide than half duplex transmission. A large number of computer applications require the computer to receive data, perform some computation and then return the results. This is essentially half duplex operation, and many interactive terminal systems are of this nature.

There are other situations, however, such as data being transmitted over a communications network (see Chapter 9), where messages travelling in opposite directions often bear no relation to each other and can therefore be transmitted simultaneously if the line is full duplex.

8.9.2 *Parallel transmission*

In parallel transmission, each bit position of a word or character code is associated with its own transmission line. Consequently all the bits of one word or one character are transmitted simultaneously. Obviously a large number of separate lines are required, and so, although it is a very fast way of transmitting data, its use is usually limited to very short-distance connections. For transmission over long distances, the cost of providing these multiple lines is usually prohibitive.

8.9.3 *Serial transmission—asynchronous*

If parallel transmission is too costly in terms of the number of lines required, the alternative is to only use one line and to send the bits that make up a character or a word one bit at a time. This is known as serial transmission.

In order that the receiving device can decode a character properly, it must know when to look for a signal and which bit is the first bit of a character. This problem is called synchronization and there are two techniques used to deal with it. The first technique, *asynchronous transmission* is suitable for low speed communications where keyboards or serial printers are directly connected to the line.

Each character transmitted is preceded by a 'start' bit and followed by at least one stop bit (hence it is sometimes called start-stop transmission). The stop bit is actually either 1, 1½ or 2 bits depending on the device and the time it needs to reset various mechanical parts.

The start bit 'wakes up' the receiver so that the receiver is aware that some data bits are following that it needs to record. The stop bits allow both the transmitting and receiving devices to get ready for the next character. They need to synchronize with each other so that the receiver samples the line at the same instant that the transmitter transmits a bit, and the stop bits allow time for this synchronization to occur.

8.9.4 *Serial transmission—synchronous*

The main drawback of asynchronous transmission is that a large proportion (about 30 per cent) of the transmitted bits are not data bits but synchronizing bits. For faster devices sending blocks of data rather than individual characters, an improved transmission technique is synchronous transmission. In this case the devices are synchronized by the transmitting of a stream of synchronizing bits at periodic intervals. In between will be blocks of data.

In order for the synchronizing bits to be distinguished from the data bits, they must be sent in a predetermined order and usually there will be a number of such timing characters (synchronizing bits) so that one of them cannot be generated as a result of random noise on the line.

The various characters that are used for synchronization and message control are described in Section 8.7.4. There is a definite sequence in which the synchronizing characters and message control characters must be transmitted, and this sequence is known as 'hand-shaking' or *protocol*. It is described in Chapter 9.

8.10 Line sharing

The provision of transmission lines, particularly over a long distance, can be very expensive. If the facilities provided by such lines can be shared between a number of devices substantial cable costs can be saved. There are a number of ways this can be done.

8.10.1 *Multiplexers*

If there are a number of devices situated near to each other but remote from the device they wish to transmit to, they can be connected with their own line to a closely situated multiplexer, which then transmits data over a single line to the remote device. Figure 8.10 illustrates such a connection. The multiplexer is responsible for transmitting information from all the

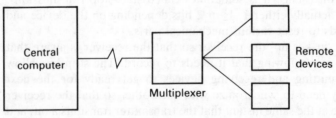

Fig. 8.10

remote devices over the single line without the information becoming mixed up. There are two ways of doing this, frequency division multiplexing (FDM) and time division multiplexing (TDM). In the case of *frequency division multiplexing* the transmission from each device is shifted to a unique frequency by the multiplexer for transmission down the line. The line then carries a number of signals (potentially up to one signal from each device, although all devices would not necessarily be transmitting simultaneously), each being transmitted simultaneously but at a different frequency. Because it is important that the frequencies do not overlap, the main disadvantage of the FDM scheme is that it does not utilize the full capacity of the line and is usually only used in relatively low speed applications where it is necessary to keep the cost to a minimum.

Time division multiplexing is achieved by transmitting blocks of characters over the line. Each remote device is allocated a character position in the block so that every block is made up of one character from each device. If a particular device is not ready to transmit a character, a null character is inserted into its position. Many TDM multiplexers are programmable machines and may even be fully programmable mini or microcomputers.

8.10.2 *Multidrop lines*

An alternative way for devices to share a line is for each device to be attached directly to the line, in such a way that only one can transmit at a time, as illustrated in Fig. 8.11.

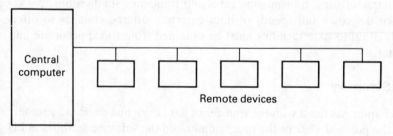

Fig. 8.11

This is known as a *multidrop network*. It is a situation similar in some ways to that encountered when attaching I/O interfaces to an I/O bus. Each device needs to have its own address so that when a message is transmitted to the remote devices only the one whose address precedes the message will respond. There also needs to be some sort of polling scheme to decide which device should transmit when a number of devices are ready to transmit. On some multidrop systems it is possible to send data to more than one device by preceding the data by a number of device addresses.

8.11 Line provision

In the United Kingdom there is a very extensive network of telecommunication facilities provided by British Telecommunications, a government regulated concern. It has a monopoly of the provision of telegraph and telephone facilities and offers data transmission facilities over both the telegraph and telephone systems under the title of 'Datel Services'. Data transmission facilities are offered over the public network of lines or over private leased lines. All the equipment, such as modems, that British Telecom supplies are manufactured by private firms under contract, but any other equipment which is to interface to the public telecommunication systems must gain approval from British Telecom. In the USA there are a large number of companies providing telecommunication facilities, although each company wishing to offer a public service must obtain approval from the Federal Communication Commission (FCC). The FCC is an independent Federal agency whose responsibilities include regulating the activities of the companies and controlling interstate and foreign facilities.

In order to ensure some degree of compatibility between transmission lines of different countries (particularly in Europe) there is an organization called the International Telecommunication Union (ITU) set up under the auspices of the United Nations Organization. One of the subgroups of the ITU which has particular relevance to the provision of data transmission facilities is the International Telegraph and Telephone Consultative Committee (CCITT) The CCITT makes recommendations on such things as line characteristics, transmission rates and frequency subdivisions.

Since the costs and speeds of lines currently offered changes so often details of up to date facilities must be obtained from the appropriate line supplier.

8.12 Summary

This chapter has dealt with the transfer of data from one device to another, from the point of view of the programmer and the software facilities at his disposal; mention has also been made of the way in which data can be transmitted over a considerable distance. For a distributed system it is necessary to look at further topics such as the possible configurations of devices on a distributed network and the various protocols necessary for preventing all the devices trying to transmit information at the same time. These ideas are really extensions of the provision of a basic data transmission facility and are discussed in Chapter 9.

The discussion of data transmission has been necessarily brief since it is intended to give the reader background knowledge of the area rather than the detailed knowledge which may be required for anyone becoming seriously involved in data transmission.

8.13 Problems

8.1 The following question requires you to use a computer to which you have low level access (machine code or assembler).

(a) Write and test a program to transfer a single character from a CPU register to the print device of a terminal.

(b) Modify the program so that it repeatedly checks the CPU register for non zero contents and outputs to the print device when non zero.

(c) Modify the program so that the character to be output is first input from the keyboard of the terminal.

(d) Modify the program to skip round the output code. What is the difference in effect now and why?

8.2 Compare and contrast the following I/O techniques:

(a) programmed I/O

(b) DMA

(c) channel processors

8.3 (a) Describe the following methods of programming data transfers between a CPU and a peripheral device:

(1) executing a program loop to examine a 'ready' status bit.

(2) using an interrupt system to interrupt the CPU when the device is ready.

(b) If a cassette tape recorder can transfer 1500 characters per second explain why it is more efficient in terms of CPU utilization to connect the cassette recorder to an interrupt driven system. Estimate the efficiency of utilization of the CPU when the cassette recorder is used in systems (1) and (2) above, stating any assumptions you make.

8.4 (a) Explain the terms

(1) remote batch processing terminals

(2) interactive terminals

(3) modems, modulation and demodulation

(4) acoustic couplers

(b) Compare and contrast time division and frequency division multiplexing. Why is multiplexing useful?

8.5 (a) Explain, using diagrams, what you understand by the following data transmission techniques

(1) simplex

(2) half duplex

(b) Explain how data can be transmitted serially using synchronous and asynchronous techniques.

(c) What is a multiplexer? Explain how time division and frequency division multiplexers work.

8.6 Assuming that for asynchronous transmission at the rate of 110 bit/s two stop bits are used (only one stop bit is used for transmission at higher speeds), when even-parity ASCII text is transmitted asynchronously at a rate of 10 characters/s over a 110 bit/s line, what percentage of the bits received actually contain data?

8.7 Given the following choice of line speeds, 110, 300, 600, or 1200 bit/s, which line speed should an asynchronous ASCII terminal use, and which does parity checking and prints at 60 characters/s?

8.8 How many ASCII characters/s can be transmitted over a 2400 bit/s line in each of the following transmission methods.
   (a) synchronous
   (b) asynchronous?

8.9 Decode the following text assuming that it is in
   (a) ASCII
   (b) EBCDIC code
   11000011 11010110 11010100 11010111 11100100
   11100011 11000101 11011001 11100010 01101101
   11000111 11011001 11000101 110000001 11100011

8.10 Fifteen terminals are connected to a computer on a multidrop line configuration. A terminal can only transmit data to the computer if the line is free. On the average, each terminal transmits data for 100 milliseconds in every 10 second period. The time required for any terminal to recognize that the line is busy is 5 milliseconds. Estimate the probability of two terminals starting transmission at the same time.

8.11 Consider the following synchronous time division multiplexing scheme. Each block commences with a framing character of 8 bits, which is used by the receiving end to identify the data from individual lines. This is followed by the characters to be transmitted, each character being 8 bits and the block containing character data from 15 different devices.
   (a) What is the effective data rate for each of the 15 devices if the transmission speed is 1200 bit/s?
   (b) If only 5 of the 15 devices wish to transmit data at any given time, what data rate can they have?

9 Distributed computing

We have now studied the computing machines which comprise the elements of a computer system. In this chapter we shall look at the next level of interconnection of these machines. We shall study how computing machines and computers may be linked to form distributed computer systems. No new hardware components are required to build such systems, but new software is required to deal with machine to machine communication.

9.1 History

Even in the 1960s all of the computing machines that made up a computer system were not necessarily sited in the same location. Many larger companies realized the need for data capture and results to be displayed at some remote site. This led to the introduction of remote job entry (RJE) terminals into many computer systems. An RJE terminal consisted (typically) of a card reader and line printer which were situated remote from the computer centre. However, the input/output devices functioned simply as batch peripherals and were connected to and driven by the central computer just like any other peripherals. An RJE station was used solely to give people who did not work in the computer centre improved access to the computing facilities.

Alongside this development, various institutions (notably the Rand Corporation), realized that a central batch facility may not be the best way to provide computing power to the users of the computing system. This led to the introduction of 'timesharing systems'. These now familiar systems allow a number of users to access computing power via slower peripherals such as teletypes or VDUs. However, due to the relative speeds of the terminals and the CPU, the structure of the operating system software had to undergo a radical change so as to allow the users to share the facilities. This is done by allowing each user, in turn, a short period of use of the facilities. As the time period is short enough, each user has the impression that he has full use of them.

Apart from the desire to take the computing power to where the users needed it there were also two developments in hardware that led directly to distributed computing. We have already seen that it is difficult to design a computer that is ideal for both input/output operations and for calculating. Thus many early large IBM systems were made up of two computers working in cooperation. The 1401 was designed as a character machine which dealt with all the input/output for the system. Connected to the 1401 was a 7094 which was a word machine and hence did all the calculation required in the system. So in these dual processor systems each computing machine was delegated to the tasks it was best able to perform, while it communicated with the other machine to complete the performance of particular tasks.

However, as the computing power was made more easily available to the user, the effect of machine failure became more catastrophic. Thus the second development on the hardware side was the introduction of two processors into a computing system. Then, if one processor failed, the other one could be switched into the system and the amount of disruption could be minimized. Often the second processor sat idle until required to perform its back-up function, but it was also possible to configure such systems so that one processor dealt with the timeshared work while the other dealt with the batch work; a failure on the timesharing processor allowed the operators to reconfigure the system and delay the batch processing.

Thus there were two major factors which led to the developments in distributed computing systems. Firstly there was the need to take the computing power to where it was required and secondly there was the need for hardware and software developments to make this possible. These two, together with continuing research, have led to an increase in the number of computing systems that can be described as distributed.

9.2 System requirements

For a computing system to be described as distributed we can identify three factors

(a) a geographical spread of equipment
(b) a geographical spread of the intelligence in the system
(c) communication between the intelligent units.

The geographical spread may be large or small and is only required so that the second factor may be present. At one extreme all the computing machines may be in one room. Such systems are based on the concept of a local area network, where a number of machines such as processors, intelligent terminals and storage devices are connected (usually on a ring as described below). At the other extreme computing machines are connected across continents (e.g., ARPA net). But although the connection technologies may be different, the basic concepts and the design aims are very similar in all distributed computing systems.

Such systems are characterized by a spread of the intelligent units; that is to say that processors or processing devices must be situated at more than one place within the system. The reasons are simply the factors noted above. In this way we can disperse the computing power to where it is required, we can increase the reliability and availability of the system as a whole and we can allow each computing machine to work on the tasks for which it was designed.

Having spread the intelligence throughout the system, we could be simply left with a number of small discrete computing systems if it were not for our third requirement that there should be interconnection and communication between the units. We shall assume that to meet our aims of reliability and availability the connection and communication must be automatic and not manual. For this reason, a distributed computing system needs special software and in particular certain protocol methods to allow the communication to take place.

In addition to the three factors mentioned, a fourth is usual but not required; this is the spread of the data throughout the system, which, if present, brings us to study distributed data bases.

9.3 Some simple examples

In banking, as in many organizations, branches deal with customers and need up-to-date information on customers' accounts; also at branch level many local administrative records and procedures must be kept, but at the centre of the organization the management and planning functions will need to have access to the same information as that used by the branches. Here two computer-based solutions seem possible. The first would be to have a large machine at the head office and to keep a database of all the records needed at the centre. Each branch could then have terminals with links to the central computer for local queries. A second solution might be to have local small computers at each branch. These local machines could then deal not only with customer accounts but also do all the required local processing. Each branch computer could then be linked to a central machine. The branch machines would only send the information required for the management function and the central machine could then process this. We shall examine later the details of system design and cost factors of such solutions, but it is likely that the distributed solution will not only prove more acceptable to the workers at the branches but also cheaper to purchase and operate. Certainly, we would expect better availability of information at the branch, and the computing power will be where it is required. It should be noted that many solutions to such an information

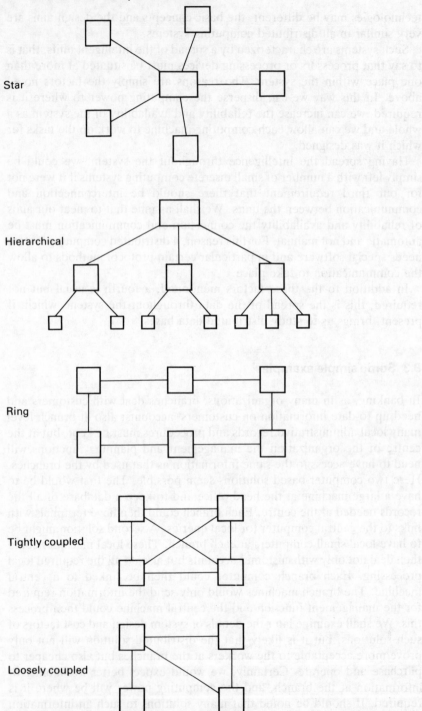

Fig. 9.1 Typical distributed computing configurations

provision are possible and each solution will have its own degree of distribution.

As a second example, let us consider the organization of a distribution company. Here it will be possible to have a relatively large machine at head office dealing with the overall planning and control function. At branch offices spread throughout the country we could have medium sized machines to deal with the routine data processing of issuing invoices, handling orders, etc. At the various distributive outlets of the company we can have small microcomputer-based intelligent terminals which check that messages are correct before they are sent to the branch offices.

This example satisfies our criteria for distributed computing systems, as the equipment is geographically spread throughout the country; the intelligence and processing is also spread and communication takes place between the computing machines. For example, communication takes place from the microcomputers which send messages on orders to the medium sized machines. The machines at the branch office will communicate back to the distributive outlets to say that the information has been accepted. Communication also takes place from the branch offices to the main office where management information is collected, processed and disseminated back to the branches and hence possibly to the distributive outlets. Computer availability is increased because if one of the branch machines should fail then at worst only some of the distributive outlets will be affected. It may even be possible either to do some degraded processing on the microcomputer or even to switch the micro to some other branch computer. Should the central machine fail, the branch machines can continue to deal with orders and either delay sending information to head office or possibly do some of the processing on the branch computer. In this example again, a large computer at head office could have dealt with terminals at both branches and distributive outlets, but such a solution seems much less preferable to our distributed computer solution. At this point the effects of either keeping all the data at head office or of distributing it to the branches should be considered.

9.4 Basic configurations

If we consider the way the computing machines are configured in our two examples above we see that they are configured in different ways. In our banking example, we have a main processor in the centre of the system with communication links radiating from it and a local computer at the end of each link. Such a system is called a *star* configuration as shown in Fig. 9.1. The distributive company's computer system is, on the other hand, a hierarchical configuration.

In Fig. 9.1, each box represents some intelligent computing machine and each line represents a communication link. The boxes are known as the *nodes* of the system. It will be seen from the figure that in a ring system each node is connected only to the ones next to it. In coupled systems, if each node is connected to each other node, the system is described as tightly coupled, while if some of the links are not present the term loosely coupled is used.

It is important to note that whether something is distributed or not may depend on the beholder. For example, each node in the diagrams of Fig. 9.1 may itself be a distributed system. In this way, it is possible to have hybrid systems built out of the basic configurations given. Consider again, for example, our banking system. At one branch the local computer could support intelligent terminals so that we have another star system at one of the points of our first star. A second branch may have its computers organized as a local ring while in the centre the large mainframe may be implemented as a set of tightly coupled computing machines.

The reasons for difference configurations and the choice of configuration for a particular requirement will depend on a multitude of factors that we consider in the next section. But for the moment let us consider our main design aim of computer power availability. In all distributed systems the major failures we can get are the failure of a communication line or the failure of a node.

In our star configuration, a line failure will mean that every machine connected to that line will be out of service, so that one of our bank branches will lose its computing link to the central machine. However, local processing may continue and all other users of the system will be unaffected. If a local node fails, again the rest of the system will continue unaffected but one branch will lose its computing power. If the central node fails, all the local processing may continue, but any communication between the local nodes is lost. It will be noted that we have assumed here that the data is also distributed. If all data is held at the centre of the system, central node failure is catastrophic. It should now be evident why we said above that our bank may well decide to implement the node at the centre as a tightly coupled system. In such a system the loss of a line or a node means that all processing may continue, albeit in a degraded fashion. However, the hardware of such a system is expensive and the software complex. Other configurations may be analysed for availability on failure in a similar way.

9.5 System design considerations

The advantages of having a distributed computing system may be classified under two headings: improvements for the people using the system and improvements in the use of the system. The advantages for the users of a distributed computing system are all refinements in the availability of computing power. We have already seen that distributed systems increase the availability by improving the technical factors of reliability.

Distributed systems are more flexible because they are more resilient and contain the effects of equipment failure; also, in the longer term, they are easier to expand as the workload increases, or to change as new technology is applied. They also allow the user to mix equipment from different suppliers, and so not only enable him to choose the best equipment for the job but also permit the use of different software packages which may only be available on one manufacturer's equipment. It is an open question whether the software is simpler and less expensive to develop and maintain. However, the major advantages in providing distributed computing systems for users lie more in the non-technical areas. Most companies have grown with a distributed management and control structure; so a distributed system fits the retention of local sovereignty. The user can take responsibility for his own data and processing, and often feels that this fits better with his requirements for job satisfaction. Indeed such systems often enable an employer to compensate people for the loss of specialist clerical skills by offering jobs which require other but similar skills.

However, there are also disadvantages in choosing a distributed system. As we shall see below, some extra software is required to allow the machines to communicate. This software of course is a one-off cost, and if it is carefully designed it need be no more expensive than software for an equally powerful large mainframe machine. A probably greater disadvantage is that of software maintenance. If the computing power is spread over different sites, the computer operations are harder to control than if all the equipment and staff are centralized. On the hardware side, field maintenance may be more expensive and indeed if we mix equipment from different suppliers it may be difficult to allocate responsibilities, but the major problem will probably be that of software maintenance. Given that it will be difficult to impose standards on the software development, it follows that the software maintenance will be a much more difficult task to undertake. However, it may be that as the system design is more modular there may, in the long run, be less software maintenance to be done. Currently there is almost no conclusive experience to draw on in this area.

The final problem with distributed systems is only a short term one and again comes from lack of experience with such systems. At the moment there are only a few agreed standards on the interconnection and passing of information between computing machines; so it is often difficult to interface machines from different suppliers. Also, we do not have, at the moment, sufficient tools to allow us to program distributed systems easily, although languages such as ADA that are designed to exploit the full power of a distributed system will soon become available.

9.6 Hardware

As stated in the introduction to this chapter, we do not need, or use, any different hardware in a distributed computer system; the problem is only to interconnect our computing machines to allow them to communicate.

We can categorize the hardware used in a distributed system into three groups: the terminals, the host computers and the communication links. Each of these groups will serve particular functions within the system.

The terminals are the user interface to the system and run the whole gamut of those considered in the other parts of this book. The choice of terminal will depend on the user interface required and may range from simple keyboards to remote batch terminals and auto-transaction terminals to sensor terminals. Indeed one distributed system uses a turnstile as a terminal in a high security library system. However, in most distributed systems, we often find that a small microprocessor has been placed within the terminal to give it some limited intelligence. In our earlier example, we saw that the messages were checked inside the terminal to ensure that they were at least clean and correct before they were sent to one of the host computers, thus leaving the computer free for the important processing. One recent idea is to allow the user to have his own *individual* interface with the computer system. The definition of this interface may be held on a floppy disk or cassette and when placed in an intelligent terminal will allow the user to use the system in the way he wants, not in the way the computer wants.

The host computers will be responsible for four major tasks. The first three of these will depend on the application for which the system is being used but will usually be a data collection subsystem, a file management subsystem and an inquiry/response subsystem. The fourth function will be the communication subsystem which will be responsible for passing messages between the computer. It is likely that software will be provided for all four areas to allow the user to develop his application.

The communication hardware between the other elements has already been discussed in detail and will use the data transmission facilities described in Chapter 8. The actual data transmitted will be carried over certain transmission carriers using the techniques discussed in the previous chapter. The transmission carriers available and used will depend on the country or countries in which the computer system is situated and the geographical spread of devices within the system. In the United Kingdom there are two principal ways of carrying data. The messages may be transmitted either over the standard switched telephone service or over private lines that it is possible to rent or lease from British Telecom using a system such as the Datel service. For longer distances, or in countries without a highly developed electronic communication system, people are experimenting with radio communication, but this is proving somewhat unreliable; and for intercontinental transmission satellites may be used.

The transmission carriers will interface with the host computers and terminals via particular machines, which may be as simple as modems or may be of the concentrator/multiplexing types. The larger distributed systems will have particular computing machines which have processing power and act as communication processors. These processors take over many of the communication functions from the host computers. They will be responsible for the handling of messages within the system, for example, they will pack and unpack messages, they will format them, schedule them, route them, monitor that they are correctly sent and received, automatically call and answer when messages are requested by other units and deal with the whole matter of handling communication between the parts of the system.

9.7 Software

In addition to the usual software of an operating system and application programs we also find, in distributed systems, a set of programs to deal with network control. At the simplest level one may purchase a standard product for network control or use the manufacturer's software to build a purpose-built program. As an example, IBM supplies a number of software tools under the general title of communication based access methods. One of these methods, telecommunication access method (TCAM), provides a macro assembler in which the message control program is coded. This message control program accesses and is accessed by the application programs in order to carry out the communication functions. Such manufacturer supplied software allows the details of the network to be hidden from the application programs by providing various facilities such as dealing with dedicated lines, polling, dialling, querying of messages, message editing, routing, coding, error correction and check-pointing. For systems with hardware communication controllers, the virtual telecommunication access method (VTAM) package allows the user to place these functions in the network control hardware and interface them with a host computer. The facilities provided by the various manufacturers differ so much in detail that it is impossible to describe them other than in outline.

9.8 Protocols

When sending the messages through the communications subsystems of a distributed computing system there must be some order in the way the messages are packaged and sent. The completely chaotic passing of messages cannot be tolerated and, we must devise a set of rules to define the messages and how they will be handled within the system. These rules are called the protocol. Protocols can occur at several levels; for example, we can have a protocol for an electrical interface which specifies how two devices should connect electrically; we can specify link control interfaces and the protocol for these, and also message handling protocol. Here we shall concentrate mainly on the data link protocols and give a broad outline of their characteristics. There are as yet no fully accepted standards for protocol usage. The international standards organizations are considering this problem, and it is expected that by the mid 1980s some sort of order will emerge from the current chaos of protocols.

In all protocols, certain control information is associated with the data to be transferred; as this control information is placed both before and after the data itself, the technique is known as 'framing' and the total information to be transferred is called a frame. The framing is done within the software for the protocol.

At the link level, the main differences between the protocols available are intended to enable users to deal with synchronous and asynchronous devices. It will be recalled that with a synchronous device we have a uniform transfer rate whereas with asynchronous devices the transfer rate is non-uniform and the message has stop and start bits associated with it.

At the link level, a number of features are associated with the protocol. Besides the framing operations, the system must also deal with line control, a feature that will specify who transmits and who receives a frame. Error control must be present to detect a frame in error and repeat the request to transfer; this will be accomplished by transmitting an error checking code with each packet. The error checking will be a more complex version of the simple parity checking we met earlier. Associated with the error checking will be some facility for timeout and startup to cater for a line being down. Some method of sequence control using packet numbers stamped with a date and time will allow for packets to arrive in the order they were sent and finally for synchronous protocols; some method of sending an idle character will be included.

A typical protocol frame is shown in Fig. 9.2. In this figure the flag is a particular bit pattern to signify start and end of frame. The address field will contain an identification of the sender and receiver so as to ensure that the correct node receives the frame and may send a reply if required;

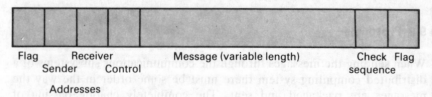

Fig. 9.2 A typical protocol frame

however, in the case of protocols designed for hierarchic systems, it is not necessary to specify the identification of the sender. The control field will specify the type of information held in the frame; this may, for example, signify that the message is information being transferred or it may signify that the frame is for control or supervisory purposes, such as frame reject, or ready to receive messages. The message field is the data itself and the check sequence allows the sender to calculate some function on the bits in the frame and then include this with the frame. The receiver will also calculate the same function on the bits and if its value corresponds with that in the check sequence all is assumed to be well with the frame.

Probably the most widely used such protocol is the IBM Synchronous Data Link Control Protocol (SDLC) which differs from Fig. 9.2 only in having one address field. It is this protocol that is the output of the VTAM system that we mentioned earlier.

9.9 Order codes for distributed computing

We saw earlier that the instruction set which is available for a given processor will allow us to process the data held in the store. While we have only one processor acting on a store this causes no problems, but in a distributed system we may well have two or more processors working on the same store at the same time. Consider the situation where two processors wish to add one to a particular store location. From our previous study of the way a processor obeys an instruction, we can see that if two processors extract the contents of the store at the same time, add one to the value at the same time, and replace the value back in store, the net effect will only be to add one to the value, although we wanted to add two to the value. This may not seem too traumatic, but consider the case of a distributed airline booking system where we sold the last seat twice. To overcome this problem of access to shared data, we need to add two further instructions to our order code. By tradition these are called P and V in honour of the Dutch computer scientist E W Dijkstra who first proposed their name and use. The store on which they operate may *only* be accessed by the P and V operations and not by any other instructions in the order code.

The V operation is simple as it will add one to the contents of the store location addressed. The P operation is somewhat more complex however. The first restriction we place on the P operation is that it must be non-interruptable; this can be implemented by making it complete its operation in one cycle time. The action of the P operation is to decrease by one the value of the store location accessed, *but* it will only do this if the value so obtained would be non-negative. If the value would go negative, the processor is not allowed to continue, but will wait until the operation is completed—this will be when some other processor obeys a V operation on the store location. While the processor is waiting it may of course be usefully employed on some other task.

To see why we define the P and V operations in this way let us consider the example shown in Fig. 9.3. The portion of a program that may change or access joint storage is called a *critical section*. In our previous example, the critical sections of both programs were the parts which add one to the variable. Thus we may code programs with critical sections by placing a P operation before the critical section and a V operation after it. Figure 9.3

Store location S initialized to 1

P(S)	P(S)
Critical section	Critical section
V(S)	V(S)
Program 1	*Program 2*

Fig. 9.3 Two programs with critical sections

shows how this is done; you should follow through both programs at once and assure yourself that only one program is obeying its critical section at any one time. Suppose the program we were writing allowed two people to access a data base *but* they could not both access it at the same time. We could then take the program outline of Fig. 9.3 and replace both critical sections by code to access the data base. Various simpler constructions which solve this problem are available in high level languages, but all these may be implemented by P and V instructions.

9.10 Costs

The cost of a computer system will vary according to the degree of distribution we put into it. There are, of course, two major items of cost to consider; these are the fixed cost of developing the system and the variable cost of running and using it. Here we shall look at the system development costs and consider how they change relative to each other as we put more or less distribution into the system. We shall not cite actual figures as these change fairly frequently, but we may expect the relative costs and the shapes of the graphs that we develop to stay the same. We shall use a costing method first proposed by the National Computing Centre in the UK, and for simplicity we shall also concentrate on star and hierarchical systems. When costing a system development, we have two main factors to consider: the software development and the cost of the hardware. The software will, as usual, consist of the design, development and implementation of the software. The hardware will comprise the costs of the system components, such as central hardware, local hardware and the data communications subsystem.

As the degree of distribution changes, the local processing costs will change as indicated in Fig. 9.4. If we have a completely centralized system,

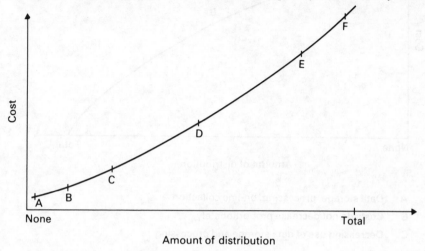

A Unintelligent terminals

B Some limited intelligence

C More software

D Use of local processor

E More local software

F Larger hardware

Fig. 9.4 Cost of local processing

the local processing cost will be almost zero, as we have only simple terminals. As we introduce limited intelligence, the local costs will increase and we shall start to incur software costs. As a computer system is placed at the local site, this and its associated software again increase the price of local processing. Figure 9.5 shows the costs for central processing which decrease as we distribute more power. With a fully centralized system we see that we need a large mainframe with large data storage, large processing and on-line connection capabilities. At (B) the costs start to decrease at the centre as we move some of the hardware and some of the software out to the remote sites, and at (C) we get a decreasing use of data processing storage at the central machine. The third graph (Fig. 9.6) shows the cost of data transmission. In a fully centralized system we need to have a high capacity leased line facility to pass the amount of information that

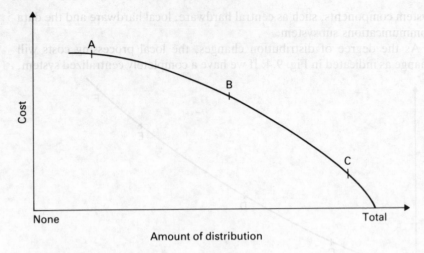

A   Data storage, processing, on-line collection
B   Costs do not decrease proportionately
C   Decreasing use of data storage and processing

Fig. 9.5 Cost of central processing

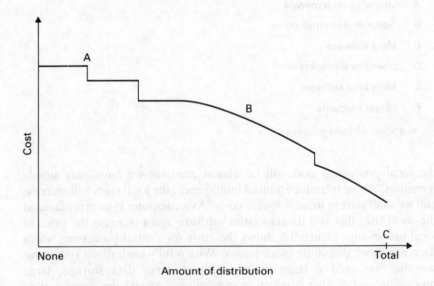

A   High capacity leased lines
B   Use of public switched network
C   No connection to central site

Fig. 9.6 Costs of data transmission

will be necessary. At (B) we can probably change to using the local public switched networks and at (C) we have no connection whatsoever to the local site; the system is totally distributed and nothing is done at the centre. Hence no data transmission is required. If we put these graphs together we obtain a graph of the shape given in Fig. 9.7 for the total costing of the

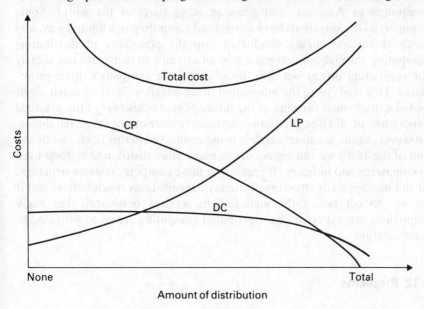

DC   Data communications
LP   Local processing
CP   Central processing

Fig. 9.7 Combined costs

system. It will be seen from this graph that a totally centralized system and a totally distributed system will probably cost more to implement than a system that is partially distributed. Again, it has been shown that the cost curves can have their minima at various points, but usually these are with some but not a lot of distribution. The variable costs of running the system are rather more difficult to present in a general form as they will often involve intangibles, such as the fact that a distributed system usually gives a better response to the user; if this is important, obviously more distribution will be brought into the system. However, the companies that have implemented distribution systems all tend to show that the amount of distribution given for the fixed costs is a feasible solution as far as the variable costs of running the system go.

9.11 Summary

So far, there is not much experience of using and building distributed computer systems. There have been a number of experimental systems such as the ARPA net which links many of the research and university computers in America, and some in other parts of the world. Some commercial organizations have distributed computing in a limited way, and much research is being conducted into the possibility of distributing computing throughout a company in an attempt to distribute not merely the computing power but also the whole of the company's office procedures. This leads us to the automated office which we hear so much about and electronic mail carrying of the future. There is also very little practical experience of distributing data, particularly distributing large databases. However, again, much research is being conducted in this field, and by the end of the 1980s we can expect to see many more distributed systems used in commerce and industry. It seems that these computer systems structures fit the management structures of many organizations much better, and if we are to get rid of the management services bottleneck that many companies are experiencing, distributed computing seems to provide the right solution.

9.12 Problems

9.1 A company has two main offices, one in Manchester and one in London. There are also various offices and warehouses throughout the UK, but each warehouse may or may not be situated at the site of its area office. Each area office is associated with a main and a subsidiary warehouse; if possible, it sends goods from its main warehouse but if this is not possible it will try to use its subsidiary warehouse. Retail outlets send orders to their local area offices and are supplied from the chosen warehouses.

Propose both a centralized and a distributed computer system for this organization. What are the advantages and disadvantages of your chosen system? State the assumptions you make about the volume of traffic in the system.

9.2 Consider the effect of either a line or a node failure in each of the configurations in Fig. 9.1. State how these differ depending on the location of data.

9.3 Visit your local computer centre or look at some manuals and find out the details of the software for teleprocessing of a given manufacturer.

9.4 In many distributed applications, a program may not pass a particular point until another has reached a particular point.

Show how this may be achieved by the use of P and V instructions.

9.5 The producer/consumer problem involves two programs, one which places items in a buffer and another which removes items from the buffer. Assuming that the buffer can hold *N* items, write two programs to perform this task.

9.6 In some distributed computing systems two processors only communicate in a master/slave relationship. Discuss the effects that this would have on a protocol used between these two machines.

9.7 Give reasons why a computer *user* might prefer either a centralized or a distributed computer system.

10 System throughput

The earlier chapters of this book have described the basic components of a computing machine, how they work and how they interact with each other. Given that the overriding factors in the design and choice of a computer system are those of reliability and cost, the other major factor is that of speed. This chapter deals with some of the techniques for improving the speed at which a computer system will work, other than improving the electrical technology of memory devices and CPU components. Improved technology has led to a dramatic increase in speed of processing over the years, but the question still remains, given a particular technology: how can the speed of the computer system be increased? Some of the techniques have already been discussed in earlier chapters. For example, if the input/output devices are made to operate concurrently with the central processing unit as in interrupt-driven programmed input/output or autonomous input/output, the CPU does not have to idle while input/output is occurring.

Performance evaluation techniques are required to measure and quantify any improvement in performance, and there are three primary areas in which performance evaluation is needed, namely design, purchase and optimization studies. A detailed discussion of all these three areas is beyond the scope of this chapter, but an introduction to some of the simpler measures of performance is a useful background to the understanding of improvement in performance.

10.1 Simple measures of performance

It is impossible to assess accurately a computer system's performance from a single parameter. For example, the cycle time of the main memory or the time to execute an add instruction have traditionally been used to indicate the power of a computer system, but these can be misleading. For example, a Hewlett Packard HP21MX minicomputer has a memory cycle time of 0.65 microseconds and an IBM 370/155 has a memory cycle time of 2.1 microseconds; yet the IBM 370/155 has a computational power greater than that of the HP21MX. Single measures can be misleading because they ignore architectural features such as, for example, word length, the way the memory may be interleaved, and cache memory.

Another measure that is often used is the number of instructions per second; often written as MIPS (millions of instructions per second). This does take into account features such as cache memory, interleaved memory, and the technique of pipelining, described in Section 10.2.5. However, it is inappropriate for vector or array processing machines (see Section 10.2.6) since a single instruction may operate on many operand fetches and stores. Here, a measure of MOPS (millions of operands per second) is sometimes used. However, all these measures ignore the word length, and so a better measure might be that of millions of bits per second, known as the *memory bandwidth*.

Rather than concentrating on the purely hardware measures of performance it is usually more helpful to measure parameters that are of interest to the users of a computer system. Typically these might be *throughput* for a batch system and *response time* for an on-line system.

The throughput measurement is an attempt to measure the gross capacity of the total system. The classic measure of this is the number of jobs processed per day or week. This takes into account all of the features of a particular computer system and is therefore much more meaningful.

Response time measurements are often used in a multi-access system to measure the length of time from a request for service until the request is completed. Many multi-access systems attempt to minimize this time in order to provide the many users with a 'fast' service.

10.2 Techniques for increasing throughput

In response to ever increasing requirements for computing systems that can handle either larger problems or more problems in less time, the design of systems has been advanced in several areas.

One major advance has been in circuit performance. Chapter 4 has already discussed the advances in memory technology and there has been a similar improvement in the circuits that are used to implement the CPU, I/O channels, etc. However, there is a limit to the advances that can be made in this area. For example, in 1950 a typical machine required 300 μs for an addition. By 1970 this was reduced to 300 ns. Is this thousandfold improvement likely to be repeated? It seems unlikely, since the speed at which electrical signals can travel will intervene. Speeds may be increased in the arithmetic and logic unit but if the execution of an instruction involves access to memory the total time is unlikely to become as small as 300 ps.

Improvements in the performance of a computer system then, must take place elsewhere. This section is concerned with various architectural features that are designed specifically to increase the throughput of a computing machine or system, other than by technological improvements.

10.2.1 *Memory bus width*

When the address of a memory location is put into the MAR and a read signal is sent to the memory, the contents of that location are transferred into the MBR.

The number of bits in the MBR, and consequently the number of bits transferred in parallel over the memory bus is called the *memory bus width*. The size of this bus is significant, because the more bits in the MBR the fewer memory cycles are needed to fetch a given amount of information and the greater the throughput. For example, doubling the memory bus width could allow two instructions to be fetched at the same time, or a double length operand to be fetched with one memory cycle. Typically, in a range of computers (e.g., the IBM 370 range or the ICL 2900 range) the slower cheaper models have fewer bits in their MBRs than the faster, more expensive models.

10.2.2 *Interleaving*

This was introduced in Chapter 4 but is also mentioned here since it is essentially a way of increasing throughput, by increasing the *effective* transfer rate of information from the memory to the CPU. Interleaving means several identical but separate memories which can operate in parallel.

Consider the example shown in Fig. 4.5. Here, four memories, each of 2^{14} words are being used to implement an address space of 2^{16} words. The 16 bit machine-level address is divided into two parts. The rightmost two bits specify the memory to be used (0, 1, 2 or 3) and the other 14 bits specify a word within that memory.

The microprogram which examines the address prior to fetching a new word, examines the rightmost two bits to select the appropriate memory. It then transfers the other 14 bits of the address to the appropriate MAR and initiates a memory read.

While waiting for that read to complete, it could use one of the other memories to fetch another word. Note that in this example four consecutive items of information (instructions or data) are all located in different memories, so that up to four words (and possibly therefore four consecutive instructions) can be fetched in parallel. For an organization having n memories, the term n-way interleaving is often used.

10.2.3 *Cache memory*

Chapter 4 introduced the concept of a cache memory. A cache memory fits in with the concept of a memory hierarchy, which is one constructed from different types of memory. By analysing programs it can be seen that in a given time the majority of programs use only a few memory locations for the storage of variables (except, perhaps, for arrays). These variables can be collected together in a special memory which is of a higher speed than the main memory, so that the execution speed of the program is increased. Such a memory is a cache memory. A more sophisticated cache memory could have a facility for ensuring that the most frequently accessed variables are held in cache. This could be achieved by keeping count of the number of accesses made to all the variables and sampling these counts at regular intervals, moving the variables between cache and main memory as necessary.

Consider the operation of a cache memory. When a read request is received from the CPU for a word in main memory, the contents of a block of words are transferred to the cache memory, and the required word is then transferred to the CPU. When any other words in this block are referenced subsequently they are transferred straight from cache.

Correspondence between main memory blocks and cache blocks is by a *mapping function*. If the cache is full and a new word is required that is not in the cache, some block in the cache is replaced with the block from memory by a *replacement algorithm*.

Consider the access to words in memory:

(a) Access to a word in cache
     Read—no difficulties;
     Write—either the cache and main memory are updated simul-
           taneously or only the cache is updated but is flagged in
           some way so that when the block is eventually removed
           the main memory is updated at this point.
(b) Access to a word not in cache
     Read—the appropriate block is brought into cache;
     Write—the word is written to directly in main memory.

To examine the possible mapping functions the following example will be used:

Main memory—64K words addressable by a 16 bit address and split into
            4K blocks of 16 bit words
Cache memory—2K words split into blocks of 16 bit words (i.e., 128
            blocks).

The simplest mapping function is the *direct mapping technique*. Here, block k of main memory maps on to block k modulo 128 of the cache memory (i.e., divide k by 128 and the remainder is the block number). Since more than one main memory block shares the same cache memory block position, contention may occur and is resolved simply by overwriting, even if the cache is not full.

A memory address is divided into three fields, a five bit tag field, a seven

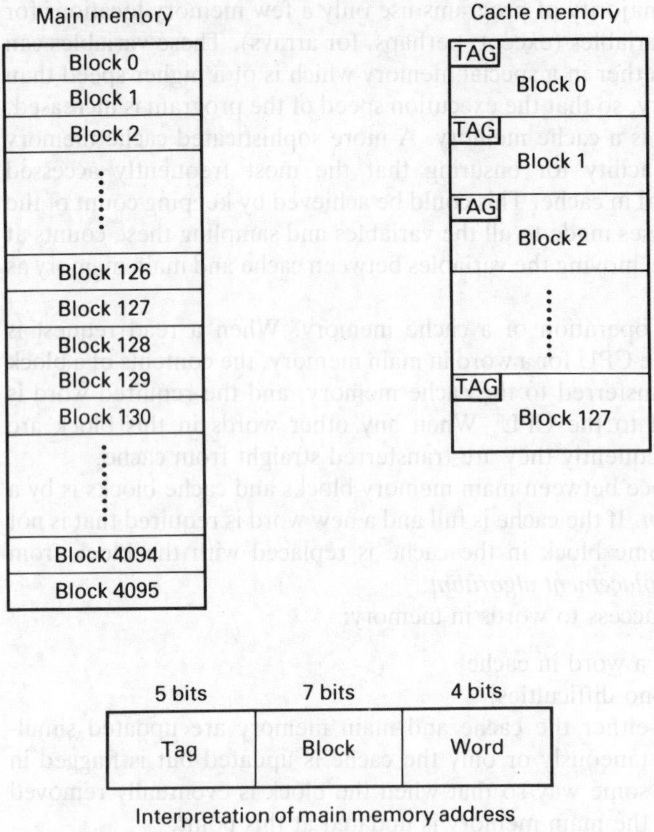

Main memory

| Block 0 |
| Block 1 |
| Block 2 |
| ⋮ |
| Block 126 |
| Block 127 |
| Block 128 |
| Block 129 |
| Block 130 |
| ⋮ |
| Block 4094 |
| Block 4095 |

Cache memory

TAG
| Block 0 |

TAG
| Block 1 |

TAG
| Block 2 |

⋮

TAG
| Block 127 |

5 bits	7 bits	4 bits
Tag	Block	Word

Interpretation of main memory address

Fig. 10.1

bit block field and a four bit word field as in Fig. 10.1. When a new block is brought into the cache memory the high order five bits are stored in the tag field of the cache block.

The following actions take place when the CPU generates a memory request.

(a) The seven bit block address field is used to address the corresponding cache block.
(b) The tag fields are then compared.
(c) If they are the same, the required word is in that block and can be accessed by using the word bits of the address. If they are not the same, the word must be accessed from main memory.

A better mapping function is known as the *associative mapping technique*. In this case, the layout of the cache memory is the same as above, except that the tag field is now twelve bits and a main memory address is

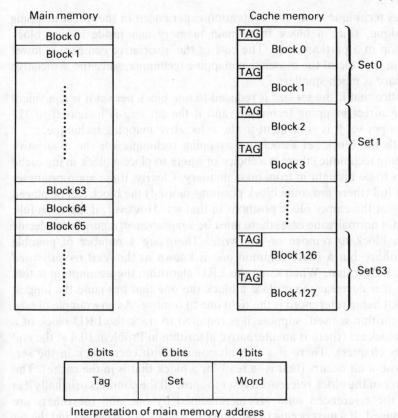

Main memory	Cache memory

Interpretation of main memory address

6 bits	6 bits	4 bits
Tag	Set	Word

Fig. 10.2

interpreted as a twelve bit tag field and a four bit word field. A block from main memory is loaded into any of the block positions in cache (usually according to some replacement algorithm). When an address is received from the CPU the high order twelve bit tag field is *associatively* compared with all the cache tag fields to see if the required block is present (see Chapter 4 for a discussion of associative stores). This technique is clearly more flexible in its use of the block positions in cache but is much more expensive because of the large associative compare.

The compromise solution often adopted is known as the *block set associative mapping technique*. In this technique, blocks are grouped into sets. Each block within a set has a tag field. A main memory address is interpreted as a tag field, a set field and a word field. The set field indicates which set the required block is in and the tag field is then associatively compared with the tag fields in that set. Figure 10.2 illustrates the situation when there are two blocks per set.

This technique eases the contention experienced in the direct mapping technique, since a block from main memory can reside in any block position in a particular set. The cost of the associative compare is lower than in the case of the associative mapping technique, since the associative compare is much smaller.

Notice that if the set size is reduced to one block per set it is equivalent to the direct mapping technique, and if the set size is increased to 128 blocks per set it is equivalent to the associative mapping technique.

With the block set associative mapping technique (or the associative mapping technique) there is a choice of where to place a block in the cache that is to be brought in from main memory. Clearly, if the appropriate set is not full (there are some block positions unused) the block can be placed in any of the empty block positions in that set. However, if the set is full, which is normally the case, there must be a *replacement algorithm* to decide which block to remove or overwrite. There are a number of possible algorithms, but a fairly common one is known as the *least recently used* (LRU) algorithm. When using the LRU algorithm the assumption is that when it is necessary to replace a block the one that has gone the longest without being referenced is the right one to remove. As an example of how an algorithm is used, suppose it is required to track the LRU block of a four block set (there is an alternative algorithm in Problem 10.4 at the end of this chapter). There is a two bit counter with each block in the set. Suppose a hit occurs (that is, a read for a block that is in the cache). The counter of the block referenced is set to zero, all the counters originally less than the referenced ones are incremented by one and the others are unchanged. If a miss occurs (a reference to a block not in cache) and the set is not full, the block is brought into the set, its counter is set to zero and the other counters are incremented by 1. If a miss occurs and the set is full, the block with a counter of 3 is removed, the new block put in its place has a counter of zero, and the other block counters are incremented by 1. It is left as an exercise for the reader to verify that this works correctly.

10.2.4 *Lookahead processors*

It can be seen from the examples in Chapter 6 that the process of fetching and executing machine instructions consists of a sequence of microinstructions. During the time of a memory access, the processor is idle (unless there are other tasks for it to do, such as incrementing the program counter). Conversely, during periods when the processor is busy, particularly when computation is proceeding in the arithmetic and logic unit, the memory access mechanism is idle. During these periods the processor could be 'looking ahead' and fetching (and perhaps decoding) the next instruction(s) so that they are already available on completion of execution of the current instruction. Clearly the number of instructions that can be *prefetched* depends on the time available, and this in turn depends on the type of instruction being processed, but between 3 and 12 instructions is quite common.

Effectively the time for execution of one instruction and the time for fetching the next instruction are overlapped and so there must be an increase in the speed at which a program is processed. The disadvantage of this approach is that it assumes the next instruction required for processing is the next one in sequence in the memory. For an unconditional branch instruction this is not true and for a conditional branch this may not be true. In both these cases the processor may be prefetching the wrong instruction. When this is discovered, during the execute phase of the branch instruction, the processor must 'throw away' the instructions that have been prefetched and continue with the correct ones. A typical example of a prefetch machine is the Prime 750. Here, the instruction prefetch unit prefetches and decodes up to four instructions from cache memory, in parallel with the processor's execution unit.

10.2.5 *Pipeline processors*

With a pipelined processor, the idea of overlapping the fetch and execute phases is extended so that each of the following phases has its own processor:
    instruction fetch
    instruction decoder
    address calculation
    data fetch
    instruction execution

This is illustrated in Fig. 10.3.

When the machine starts, the first instruction is fetched by the instruc-

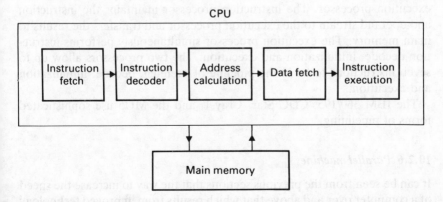

Fig. 10.3

tion fetch unit. After that, the instruction decoder will decode this first instruction while the instruction fetch unit is fetching the second instruction. The next step will be to make the address calculation for the first instruction, decode the second instruction and fetch the third instruction, all in parallel. Clearly the potential throughput of such a pipelined machine must be greater than that of a sequential machine because of all the concurrent operations. However, it requires much more complex hardware to ensure the correct timing of all the operations on the pipeline. There is also the same problem of branch instructions as on a lookahead machine (in fact, a lookahead machine is a very simple pipelined machine). If a control transfer occurs as a result of either an unconditional branch instruction, or a conditional branch instruction for which the condition is met, then all the prefetched instructions must be abandoned. Thus a large gap appears in the instruction stream. The net effect of this on the performance of the processor depends on the frequency with which branch instructions occur, and a number of studies of the performance of computer systems indicate that this may be as high as 20 per cent of all instructions obeyed.

A possible modification of the pipeline to ease this problem is to have a number of special buffer registers which contain the first few instructions at the destination or 'branched-to' addresses of recently obeyed control transfer. Access to these registers is via an associative search on the addresses of the instructions they contain. The pipeline mechanism proceeds normally until a branch occurs and the destination address is then presented to the associative store. If a match is found, the appropriate instructions are extracted and discharged into the pipeline. If no match is found, there is a hold up while instructions are fetched from memory, and the buffer registers are updated with these instructions also.

An example of a machine with a pipeline facility is the Harris 800. This computer has two separate processors, the instruction processor and the execution processor. The instruction processor maintains the instruction and operand stream to the execution processor and transfers the results to main memory. The execution processor simultaneously performs instruction decode, initialization and execution. The two processors allow up to seven instructions to be in the pipeline of prefetch, decode, initialization and execution.

The IBM 360/195, CDC Star, Cray-1, and the MU5 use sophisticated forms of pipelining.

10.2.6 *Parallel machines*

It can be seen from the previous sections that the way to increase the speed of a computer over and above that which results from improved technology is to introduce parallelism into its operation.

A useful classification of parallel computer systems, known as the Flynn Classification, makes use of the ideas of parallelism in the instruction stream and parallelism in the data stream. The instruction stream is the sequence of instructions that are executed in a processing unit. The data stream is the sequence of operands being manipulated. There are four classes of parallel computer systems, illustrated in Fig. 10.4.

SISD is a single instruction, single data stream machine. At any given time during execution of a program, there is at most one instruction being executed, and that instruction affects at most one piece of data. This is the type of computing machine described in the earlier chapters of this book.

SIMD is a single instruction, multiple data stream machine. At any given time during execution of a program, there is at most one instruction being executed, but it affects an array of data (a data vector) rather than a single operand. For example, a weather prediction program might read hourly temperature measurements taken from five hundred weather stations and then compute the daily average at each station by performing exactly the same computation on each set of twenty four hourly readings. For each station it would load the first value into a register then add the second value and the third and so on, finally dividing the sum by twenty four. Since the same program is used on each data set, a processor with one PC and one instruction decoder but N arithmetic units and N register sets could carry out computations on N data sets simultaneously. This type of processor is also sometimes known as an *array processor*. A common example of a SIMD system is the associative store described in Chapter 4. The same task (in this case a comparison) is performed on every word in the store in parallel.

MISD is a multiple instruction, single data stream. Each operand is operated on by several instructions simultaneously. This does not seem to be a useful concept.

MIMD is a multiple instruction, multiple data stream computer. There are n instruction streams and n data streams, one data stream per instruction stream. Because there are n processors, there needs to be some form of communication between them, so that they can co-operate within the required processing. The MIMD organization can be implemented so that all the data share the same primary memory (a multiprocessor organization), or each processor has its own primary memory (a multi-computer organization).

Even a simple computing machine with a DMA or channel processor (see Chapter 8) is a MIMD system. The main CPU and the DMA processor are processing in parallel, each with their own data stream.

A typical MIMD system that is now very common is that of a distributed system or network. Here, there are a number of processors each processing their own data stream and communicating with each other over the network communication system (see Chapter 9).

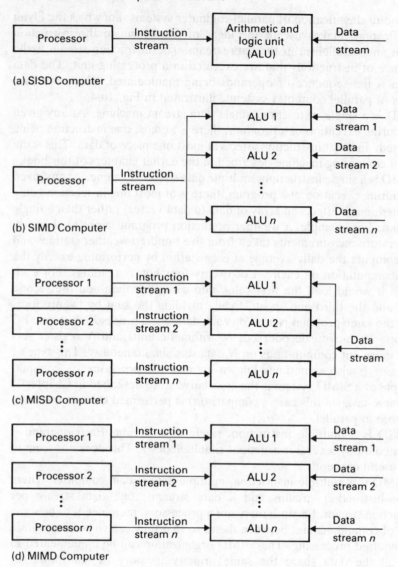

Fig. 10.4

A special case of this distributed function organization is the pipeline described in Section 10.2.5. Suppose we have a process P made up of two subprocesses P1 and P2. If both are executed on a single processor, the time the processor is occupied is $t_1 + t_2$ units. With a pipeline machine the processor is free to start a new task every max (t_1, t_2) time units. Thus the throughput is increased, although the complete problem still takes $t_1 + t_2$ time units to complete.

Pipelining does not provide more throughput than an equivalent parallel organization. If two MIMD processors each execute P1 and P2, then a new problem can be executed every $(t_1 + t_2)/2$ time units on average. The pipeline can do no better then this because

$$\max(t_1, t_2) \geq (t_1 + t_2)/2$$

However, in a pipeline machine the processors are dedicated to a particular task and so may be less expensive to produce.

10.3 Summary

One method of making a computer 'faster' is to improve the technology of its component parts. There has been a dramatic improvement in this area over the last thirty years. However, it is still worth while investigating different techniques for combining these components and organizing the architecture, since there are valuable gains to be made over and above that provided by new technology. This chapter has identified some of the more important (from the very simple to the complex) techniques that have been developed.

10.4 Problems

10.1 A computer with a cache memory uses the direct mapping technique for cache organization. The following are the pertinent parameters.

Main memory	64K words with a cycle time of 10 μs.
Cache memory	1K words with a cycle time of 1 μs.
Block size	128 words

Specify the number of bits in the tag, block and word fields in the interpretation of main memory addresses.

10.2 A block set associative cache consists of a total of 64 blocks divided into 4 block sets. The main memory contains 4K blocks, each block consisting of 128 words.
   (a) How many bits are there in the main memory address?
   (b) How many bits are there in each of the tag, set and word fields?

10.3 Suppose that the machine described in Problem 10.1 is used to run a program consisting of 2800 instructions each held in one word, which are all executed in simple sequence.

Estimate the instruction fetch time for the whole program for both the machine with cache and the machine without cache. Explain the results.

10.4 Consider the following LRU algorithm for a cache with B blocks. The cache hardware maintains a B × B matrix, with the rows and columns numbered 1 through B. Whenever block n is referenced, row n is set to all 1s. After that step, column n is set to all 0s. At any point in time, the row with the lowest value (read as a binary number) is the least recently used row. Show that this algorithm works for a four block cache and the following sequence of block references

$$1 \quad 2 \quad 3 \quad 4 \quad 4 \quad 4 \quad 2 \quad 3 \quad 1 \quad 3 \quad 4 \quad 2 \quad 1 \quad 3 \quad 4 \quad 4$$

10.5 A program consists of two nested loops, a small inner loop and a much larger outer loop.

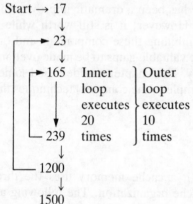

Start → 17

23

165   Inner loop executes 20 times   Outer loop executes 10 times

239

1200

1500

The numbers shown are the decimal addresses which indicate the start and end of both loops. All memory locations in sections 17–22, 23–164, 165–239, etc., contain instructions to be executed in straight line sequence.

The program is to be run on a computer that has a cache memory. The cache is organized in the direct mapping manner as follows

Main memory   64K words with a cycle time of 10 μs.
Cache memory   1K words with a cycle time of 1 μs.
Block size is 128 words.

(a) Ignoring operand and result fetching and storing, compute the total amount of time needed for instruction fetching in the above program.

(b) Repeat the above calculation assuming no cache is available.

10.6 A salesman extols the virtue of his company's latest computer which boasts:
  (a) a pipeline consisting of instruction fetch and execution processors;
  (b) a provision of virtual memory; and

(c) cache memory.

Discuss the merits or otherwise of these features.

10.7 Discuss, and give examples of, the Flynn classification scheme for parallel computer systems, SISD, SIMD, MISD, MIMD. Explain how a pipelined machine fits into such a classification.

10.8 Review the architectural features of a computer system that are designed to increase throughput.

Appendix 1

A1.1 Number systems

Although in everyday life, people generally use the decimal number system for counting, it is more convenient to use the binary number system in a computer, since, as explained in Chapter 4, electronic components are usually in one of two states, which can be used to represent 0 and 1, the two digits used in the binary number system.

The binary system can perhaps be best explained by considering first a typical number in the decimal system. This system uses ten symbols 0 to 9. The weighting of each digit is a power of ten determined by the position of the digit within the number and consequently decimal numbers are said to be to the base ten.

For example, the decimal number 4528.035 is made up as follows:

$$4 \times 10^3 \;+\; 5 \times 10^2 \;+\; 2 \times 10^1 \;+\; 8 \times 10^0 \,.\, 0 \times 10^{-1} \;+\; 3 \times 10^{-2} \;+\; 5 \times 10^{-3}$$

(1000s)   (100s)   (10s)   (units)   (0.1s)   (0.01s)   (0.001s)

Decimal
point

Remember that any number raised to the power of zero is 1. The binary number system (base 2) uses 2 digits (*binary digits* or bits) 0 and 1 and a number has the same structure as a decimal number except that the weighting of each digit is a power of two.

Thus $101101 = 1 \times 2^5 + 0 \times 2^4 + 1 \times 2^3 + 1 \times 2^2 + 0 \times 2^1 + 1 \times 2^0$
which is equivalent to 45 in the decimal system.

Other number bases encountered are octal (base 8) and hexadecimal (base 16). These are of importance because they can be used as a 'shorthand' for binary numbers. This is because three binary digits can be represented by the numbers 0 to 7, i.e., the octal range, while four binary digits can be represented by the numbers 0 to 15, i.e., the hexadecimal range (see Fig. A.1).

The representation of a digit in the hexadecimal system creates a problem, since, if the normal decimal numerics were used, two characters would be needed to represent each of the values 10 to 15. This is overcome by using letters to extend the representation of numbers, i.e., A $\equiv$ 10, B $\equiv$ 11, . . ., F $\equiv$ 15 (see Fig. A.1).

As an example of a number expressed in these different number bases, consider the decimal number 1984 represented in binary, octal and hexadecimal.

Binary

$$1 \quad\quad 1 \quad\quad 1 \quad\quad 1 \quad\quad 1 \quad\quad 0$$
$$(1 \times 2^{10} + 1 \times 2^9 + 1 \times 2^8 + 1 \times 2^7 + 1 \times 2^6 + 0 \times 2^5$$

$$0 \quad\quad 0 \quad\quad 0 \quad\quad 0 \quad\quad 0$$
$$+ \; 0 \times 2^4 + 0 \times 2^3 + 0 \times 2^2 + 0 \times 2^1 + 0 \times 2^0)$$

Octal

$$3 \quad\quad 7 \quad\quad 0 \quad\quad 0$$
$$(3 \times 8^3 + 7 \times 8^2 + 0 \times 8^1 + 0 \times 8^0)$$

Hexadecimal

$$7 \quad\quad C \quad\quad 0$$
$$(7 \times 16^2 + 12 \times 16^1 + 0 \times 16^0)$$

Section A1.2 explains the processes involved in converting from one number base to another.

The usefulness of octal or hexadecimal representation as a shorthand for binary numbers can be seen from the above example. The binary system results in numbers with a large number of digits. On paper this can be more conveniently expressed by the octal or hexadecimal systems which require fewer digits.

Note now that since some numbers could equally well be a number in decimal, binary, octal or hexadecimal, for example 101, it is usual to signify the base in which the number is represented by writing, for example, 101_2 for binary or 101_8 for octal.

A1.2 Conversion between the number systems

Figure A.1 lists some examples that may be useful in converting numbers from one base to another.

A1.2.1 *From binary to octal*

Any octal digit can be represented by 3 binary digits (see Fig. A.1). Consequently, to convert a binary number to octal, simply divide the binary number into groups of 3 binary digits, starting at the decimal point (and working both ways if it is a fractional number) and represent each group by its equivalent octal digit.

Decimal n	Binary	Octal	Hexadecimal	2^n
0	0	0	0	1
1	1	1	1	2
2	10	2	2	4
3	11	3	3	8
4	100	4	4	16
5	101	5	5	32
6	110	6	6	64
7	111	7	7	128
8	1000	10	8	256
9	1001	11	9	512
10	1010	12	A	1024
11	1011	13	B	2048
12	1100	14	C	4096
13	1101	15	D	8192
14	1110	16	E	16384
15	1111	17	F	32768

Fig. A.1

Consider again the earlier example of the binary equivalent of 1984_{10}.

Binary	11	111	000	000
Octal digits	3	7	0	0

To convert from octal to binary is exactly the reverse procedure. Replace each octal digit by its 3 bit binary equivalent.

A1.2.2 *From binary to hexadecimal*

This is very similar to the octal conversions, except that each hexadecimal digit is represented by 4 binary digits. Consequently it is necessary to divide the binary number into groups of 4 digits and replace each of these by their equivalent hexadecimal value; the reverse procedure is used to convert from hexadecimal to binary.

Referring once more to our example of the binary equivalent of 1984_{10}, we have

Binary	111	1100	0000
Hexadecimal digits	7	C	0

A1.2.3 *From binary to decimal*

To convert a number from decimal to binary, one of two methods can be used. One method is to consider the composition of a binary number as defined in Section A1.1. The number to be converted must be decomposed into its various powers of 2 corresponding to bit positions.

For example, the decimal number

24.625 is made up of

$$1 \times 16 \quad (2^4)$$
$$1 \times 8 \quad (2^3)$$
$$0 \times 4 \quad (2^2)$$
$$0 \times 2 \quad (2^1)$$
$$0 \times 1 \quad (2^0)$$
$$1 \times 0.5 \quad (2^{-1})$$
$$0 \times 0.25 \quad (2^{-2})$$
$$1 \times 0.125 \; (2^{-3})$$

Consequently the binary equivalent is

1 1 0 0 0 . 1 0 1

An alternative method, which will only work for integer decimal numbers, is to divide the number by 2 repeatedly. The remainder at each stage (either a 0 or a 1) gives the next bit in the binary equivalent. As an example, consider the decimal number 207.

Quotient	Remainder	
207		
103	1	rightmost bit
51	1	
25	1	
12	1	
6	0	
3	0	
1	1	
0	1	leftmost bit

The resulting binary number is 11001111

To convert binary to decimal sum up the powers of 2 that correspond to 1 bits in the binary number. As an example, refer to the conversion of a binary number in Section A1.1.

A1.3 The representation of numeric information

A1.3.1 *Integer numbers*

A decimal integer (whole number) can simply be converted to its equivalent binary value and stored in memory as the contents of, say, one word.

However, if, as is usual, it is required to store negative numbers, some way has to be found of storing the sign. There are a number of ways, but two of the most common are sign and magnitude and two's complement.

A1.3.1.1 *Sign and magnitude*

With sign and magnitude representation the most significant bit of the word is used to indicate the sign (0 represents positive and 1 represents negative). The remainder of the word holds the absolute magnitude of the number. For example, in a 16 bit word, the values $+ 11$ and $- 14$ would be represented as

$$\text{sign} \begin{cases} 0000000000001011 \quad + 11 \\ 1000000000001110 \quad - 14 \end{cases}$$

One of the disadvantages of such a representation is that there are two representations for zero, $+ 0$ and $- 0$.

A1.3.1.2 *Two's complement*

With this representation a positive number is stored with a sign bit (the most significant bit) of 0, the remainder of the word containing the binary value of the number.

A negative number, however, is stored as the two's complement of the binary pattern of the equivalent positive number. To obtain the two's complement of a binary number, replace all zeros by ones and all the ones by zeros (i.e., flip the bits) and add 1. For example consider the 8 bit representation of the number -4.

$$\begin{aligned} \text{Take the two's complement of} \quad & 00000100 \\ = \; & 11111011 \\ & \quad\quad\;\; + 1 \\ = \; & 11111100 \end{aligned}$$

The most significant bit is still the sign bit, a 1 indicating a negative number.

There are two advantages of this representation. First, there is only one representation of 0 and this is $+0$. Secondly, in order to perform the computation of subtraction such as $A - B$, the two's complement of B is added to A. Thus the arithmetic unit of the CPU only needs to be able to complement (a simple bit flipping operation) and add. Consider as an example the calculation of $3 - 2$

$$\begin{aligned} = \; & 00000011 - 00000010 \\ = \; & 00000011 + \text{two's complement of } 00000010 \\ = \; & 00000011 + 11111110 \\ = \; & 00000001 \text{ (the carry bit beyond the end of the word is} \\ & \quad\quad\quad\quad\quad \text{discarded).} \end{aligned}$$

Clearly this is the value $+1$.

If the result of an operation involving two numbers exceeds the maximum number allowed, overflow has occurred. This can be detected by examining the carry bit (which is normally discarded) after an arithmetic operation has been performed.

As an example, consider the sum of two 4 bit unsigned numbers (which must be in the range 0 to 15).

$$
\begin{array}{r}
1001 \quad (9 + 8 = 17) \\
+ \ 1000 \\
\hline
10001
\end{array}
$$

Here, the result (17) is larger than can be contained in 4 bits and the carry bit (1 in this example) indicates that overflow has occurred. However, with signed numbers, setting the carry bit to 1 does not always indicate overflow because the carry notation can become confused with that used for negative numbers (two's complement). For example, if we use two's complement notation to represent a negative number, the calculation of -3 and -2 would result in a carry bit of 1, but the result could easily be stored in 4 bits, even with one bit indicating the sign.

When manipulating two numbers where negative numbers are stored in two's complement form, overflow has occurred if the two numbers being added have the same sign and the result has the opposite sign.

A1.3.2 *Floating point numbers*

In mathematical notation, a representation of numbers known as floating point notation is commonly used, particularly to represent very large or very small numbers. For example, as already mentioned, the mass of a hydrogen atom is 1.660×10^{-24} grams. Because the range of numbers that can be represented by integer notation is limited by the word length, floating point notation is convenient for representing non integer numbers (often referred to as 'real' numbers) in a computer.

The following examples show the floating point representation of some 'real' numbers.

$$
\begin{array}{rcl}
562.428_{10} &=& 0.562428 \times 10^3 \\
- \ 62.018_{10} &=& -0.62018 \times 10^2 \\
0.000527_{10} &=& 0.527 \times 10^{-3} \\
110.11011_2 &=& 0.11011011 \times 2^3 \\
0.00101101_2 &=& 0.101101 \times 2^{-2}
\end{array}
$$

Such numbers can be represented as

$$
\pm \ m \times r^e
$$

where m is known as the mantissa, r the radix, and e the exponent.

Within a computer, a binary floating point number can be represented by storing the values of m and e, the radix being assumed. Consider the following example:

0.11011011×2^3

Only the values 11011011 and 3

need be stored, the others being assumed. In fact if the mantissa is adjusted so that the first digit to follow the assumed point is a 1, the number is said to be *normalized* and this 1 need not be stored. (Obviously the arithmetic and logic unit needs to be aware of it in order to perform the computations correctly.)

On the assumption that 32 bits are available (either a 32 bit word or two 16 bit words), a typical representation of a floating point number in a computer would be as follows:

Mantissa	Exponent
24 bits	8 bits

The mantissa can be stored in either sign and magnitude form or two's complement form, as in the case of integer numbers. In practice, since special hardware (or software) is necessary to perform computations on floating point numbers, there is no particular advantage in using the two's complement form; so the use of sign and magnitude is not uncommon.

With the exponent, however, a representation known as *excess* form is often used. For N bit numbers, the value is stored as the sum of itself and 2^{N-1}. For example, for $N = 8$ (the size of the exponent used in the earlier example) the system would be called *excess 128* and the exponent would be stored as its true value plus 128. Since, for 8 bit exponents, the value of the exponent could lie between -128 and $+127$, storing it in excess 128 form means that the value lies between 0 and 255. The main advantage to be gained is that because the exponent usually only occupies part of a word its value will have to be extracted by using a suitable mask and logical AND instruction (see Chapter 5). If it were extracted and left in a word greater in size than 8 bits, the leading bits would be zero, and would have to be changed if the number had been negative in order to maintain the two's complement form of representation. With the excess form, no such change has to take place, the exponents always being positive. Consequently, processing of the number will be faster. When printing out a result, the binary floating point number will have to be converted to decimal, and it is an easy task at that stage to subtract 128 from the exponent.

The example discussed used 32 bits to store a floating point number. Although this is common, many machines provide facilities for defining 64 bit, 128 bit or even 60 bit and 120 bit floating point numbers. Increasing the number of binary digits available for storing the mantissa will clearly increase the accuracy to which a number can be stored. Increasing the number of binary digits available for storing the exponent will increase the range of numbers that can be stored.

A1.4 Problems

1. Convert the following decimal numbers to the equivalent binary numbers:

   (a) 14   (b) 13   (c) 15
   (d) 6   (e) 21   (f) 19
   (g) 63   (h) 103   (i) 256
   (j) 0.4375   (k) 512.5   (l) 131.5625

2. Convert the following binary numbers to equivalent decimal numbers:

   (a) 1101   (b) 1001   (c) 10111
   (d) 1011   (e) 11011   (f) 10101
   (g) 0.1011   (h) 111011.1011   (i) 11.01010111

3. Perform the following additions and check by converting the binary numbers to decimal and adding:

   (a) 1001.1 + 1011.11   (b) 100101 + 100101
   (c) 0.1011 + 0.1101   (d) 1011.01 + 1001.11

4. Perform the following subtractions in binary and check by converting the numbers to decimal and subtracting:

   (a) 1111 − 1000   (b) 1101 − 1011   (c) 1011.1 − 111.1
   (d) 1111.01 − 1011.1 (e) 111.11 − 111.1   (f) 1101.1 − 1110.01

5. Convert the following hexadecimal numbers to decimal:

   (a) B6C7   (b) 64AC   (c) A492   (d) D2763

6. Convert the following octal numbers to decimal:

   (a) 14   (b) 124   (c) 105
   (d) 123   (e) 156   (f) 15.5

7. Convert the following binary numbers to octal:

   (a) 101101   (b) 101101110   (c) 10110111
   (d) 110110.011   (e) 011.1011011

8. Convert the following octal numbers to binary:

   (a) 56   (b) 43   (c) 231.2
   (d) 231.4   (e) 454.45   (f) 32.234

9. Convert the following decimal numbers to octal:

   (a) 15   (b) 9   (c) 19
   (d) 0.54   (e) 0.625   (f) 2.125

10. Convert the following hexadecimal numbers to binary:

    (a) CD   (b) 649   (c) A13   (d) AA   (e) ABCDE

11. Convert the following binary numbers to hexadecimal:

    (a) 10110111   (b) 10011100   (c) 1011111
    (d) 0.01111110   (e) 101011.1011001

12. To convert a decimal integer X, whose value lies between 0 and 32767, into a 15 bit binary number, the following algorithm can be used:
    (a) Is $X \geq 16384$? If so, set the most significant bit to 1 and subtract 16384 from X. Otherwise, set the most significant bit to zero and omit the subtraction step.
    (b) Repeat step (a) using one half of the previous test constant to determine the next significant bit.
    (c) Repeat until 15 bits have been obtained.
    Write and test a program to implement the above algorithm.

13. Find the two's complement of the following binary numbers:
    00110101 and 01000000.

14. Add the binary number 01010000 to each of the two's complement numbers computed in Problem 13. Verify the results by converting all binary numbers to decimal and reworking the calculations in decimal.

15. Repeat Problems 4(a) and 4(b) using the two's complement number system.

16. Consider the following addition problems for three bit binary numbers in two's complement. For each sum, determine whether
    (a) the sign bit of the result is 1.
    (b) the low-order three bits of the result are 0.
    (c) overflow has occurred.

000	000	111	100	100
001	111	110	111	100

17. (a) Describe one of the methods commonly used for representing signed integers in present-day digital computers. What are the maximum and minimum values which may be represented by your method?
    (b) Express the contents of the 32 bit word containing hexadecimal 008150C1 as:
    (a) four EBCDIC characters
    (b) a fixed point integer decimal number.

How is a computer able to distinguish between the two?

(c) The following two integers have been printed in their binary coded decimal (BCD) representation. Convert them to a normalized floating point representation using 6 bits for the mantissa and 5 bits for the exponent.
Number 1: 000100011001
Number 2: 00100000

18. Determine the accuracy and range of numbers stored in floating point format by using the representation described in this appendix. What would be the effect on accuracy and range if the number of available bits were increased to 64 bits, the exponent remaining at 8 bits?

19. (a) (1) Represent each of the decimal values 26, -37, 19909 in their fixed point number format, assuming a word length of 16-bits.
   (2) How would the words created in (1) above be interpreted as ASCII characters and EBCDIC characters?

(b) What is meant by the term 'floating point number'? Explain how a floating point number may be represented by a fixed point mantissa and an exponent, indicating particularly the effect on range and accuracy of your representation.

Appendix 2 A computer system simulator

It is apparent that students only fully appreciate the differences in computer architecture when they are able to have 'hands on' experience. The computer system simulator, which operates at the register transfer level, allows them to gain experience of many different architectures without recourse to a multiplicity of computers. This experience, in the first instance, is gained by their being able to run programs on the simulated computers and observe the state of the computer after each machine or micro-instruction. The design of the teaching computers is chosen so that each demonstrates a particular architectural detail. Subsequently students can design their own computer systems and compare them with simulations of commercially available computers.

A2.1 Introduction

Even though students can be given examples of programs to write for different types of computer, it is better if they can have some actual experience of programming them. Hence there is a need for a simulator that is sufficiently flexible to allow many different types of computer to be simulated. Further, the process of defining the simulated computer and the execution of programs together with associated output has useful educational value. That is, the students should be able to learn not only by the running of programs but also by using the simulator.

The requirements are:

(a) a flexible means of simulating many different computer architectures;
(b) a definition process which reinforces course material;
(c) sufficient relevant output, so that a sensible investigation of what the computer has done is possible and improvements in its design can be formulated;
(d) an implementation which allows easy alteration as new facilities become necessary.

A design aim is that the simulator should operate at the register transfer level. There are three main reasons for this. First, the simulator will use basic building blocks that are common to all computers and will therefore be flexible in its applicability. Secondly, there are few developments of functionally new building blocks at the register transfer level; thus there should be little need to change the simulator. For example, it does not matter what technology is used to implement a memory because it will have the same functionality regardless. Thirdly, at this level, architectural developments and design decisions can be more fully investigated because of the relationship between design and the computer's micro-instruction set. A micro-instruction defines the transfer of data from one hardware component to another. The set of micro-instructions depends directly upon the components used at the register transfer level. However, the set of micro-instructions is not limited by the set of components, because many different micro-instruction sets can be generated by the same set of components. Hence the analysis and design aspects of computer architecture can be more easily explained.

It would appear, therefore, that the choice of register transfer level will satisfy the first requirement. In part it also satisfies the final requirement, in that the frequency of changing the simulator will be reduced. Further, when changes are required, only the functionality will have to be simulated, and this will, hopefully, be a simpler matter than if a lower level, closer to the electronics, had been chosen.

The second and third requirements can only be satisfied by the adoption of an appropriate specification for the simulator. This aspect of the simulator will now be discussed.

A2.2 The specification of the simulator

The specification of the simulator can be broken down into three parts, namely: component specification, micro-instruction specification and the output from the simulator. It is not necessary to discuss the input information to the simulator because it will be very closely related to the parameters chosen for the specification of components and micro-instructions.

A2.2.1 *Hardware components*

The components that can be described by the simulator are: registers, flip-flops, slow peripheral channels, stores and stacks. It was decided not to simulate the bus structure explicitly but by the amount of concurrent operation of micro-instructions. That is, if micro-instructions can execute concurrently, there must be a bus structure which supports that concurrency. If, in a particular system being simulated, the bus structure is required explicitly, it can be simulated either by using a register or channel component.

A *register* is a collection of bits which are referenced by a name. The register has associated with it a length indicating the number of bits, and a time indicating how long it takes to process information in the register. The bits are numbered such that the leftmost or most significant bit is zero. This is counter to some engineering standards, but, as has already been indicated, this is the lowest level of computer architecture to which students are exposed at length, and they tend to think left to right. Bit numbering is required, because parts of registers can be processed in some micro-instructions.

A *flip-flop* is a one bit component which can hold either the value one or zero. It is referenced by a name. It has a time associated with its use.

A *channel* is a means of transferring data to and from the outside world via a slow peripheral. It is referenced by a name and has an associated width (the number of bits then can be transferred in parallel), and a time. Such slow peripherals do not operate at a constant rate, and hence the time must be chosen so that the average delay generated when using a channel can be included when the time for execution is calculated. It was decided not, at this stage anyway, to simulate fast disk channels. This would necessarily require some form of parallel operation and it was not felt that the complexity introduced would be worthwhile.

A *store* is an ordered collection of registers, the whole collection being referenced by a name. Individual registers are referenced by specifying the name and the index of the register required. A store has attributes of the amount of time needed to read or write information into a register of the store, the number of bits in an individual register and the names of two registers which will act as buffer and address registers. The address register holds the index of the location of the store register to be accessed. The buffer register either holds a value to be placed in the store at the address specified during write access, or receives data during read access.

A *stack* is similar to a store except that the address register has associated with it an adder which predetermines the address of the next access. Other than this the attributes are the same as for a store.

A2.2.2 *Micro-instructions*

The set of micro-instructions was chosen so that it would be possible to carry out many operations upon the hardware components. At the register transfer level, information is transferred from one component to another with, possibly, some modification taking place during the course of the transfer. No hardware components such as adders and shift registers have been specified. The functionality of these components has been included in the micro-instructions. For example, an arithmetic operation is effected when the contents of two registers are transferred to a third register. Such a micro-instruction will obviously have a delay that is greater than a simple transfer from one register to another.

Each micro-instruction generates a delay which is used to form both a time for the particular machine instruction and the complete execution time for the program. This delay is generated in one of three ways. First, it may arise from the times associated with the hardware components. Secondly, it may occur as a result of the micro-instruction itself having its own inherent delay, such as the time for an arithmetic operation or shift. Finally, the micro-instruction may cause no delay, because it proceeds concurrently with another micro-instruction which causes the delay. The bus structure used must be able to reflect this concurrency.

A brief description of the complete set of micro-instructions is presented so that an idea of the level of the simulator can be appreciated.

Transfer causes the contents of a register or channel to be transferred to another register or channel. Parts of the sending or receiving components can be specified, in which case the remainder of the receiving component will be zero. If the sending component is a register its contents remain unaltered. In the case of a channel, the next value from the data input stream will be placed in the channel.

Overwrite is essentially the same as a transfer, except that parts of the components are always specified and the contents of the receiving component will be overwritten, the remainder being unaltered.

Read causes a store to be accessed so that the contents of the location specified by the address register are placed in the buffer register.

Write causes the contents of the buffer register, of a store, to be placed in the location specified by the address register.

Push and *pop* have the same effect as read and write except that they operate upon stacks.

Arithmetic operations, *add, subtract, multiply* and *divide* cause the contents of two registers to be operated upon by the chosen operation and the result is placed in a third register. A check is made for result overflow and underflow as necessary. This is indicated by a flip-flop identified in the instruction being set. The value of the flip-flop can then be tested by a subsequent micro-instruction. Floating-point arithmetic has not been implemented because it is not especially relevant to the overall discussion of a computer's architecture. It is, however, very important when the structure of an adder unit is being developed.

Test allows the value of a register or flip-flop to be examined and its value compared with a literal value specified in the micro-instruction. If the result of the comparison is false, a number of succeeding micro-instructions are not obeyed. This number is specified in the test micro-instruction together with the literal value and the comparison to be carried out ($<$, $<=$, $=$, $\neq$ $>=$, $=$). It si not possible to compare the contents of two registers directly.

Branch causes a micro-instruction and following sequence to be obeyed when they are not in the normal sequence of micro-instruction operation. The micro-instruction to which the jump is made is indicated by a signed integer. The integer gives the relative displacement of the next micro-instruction to be obeyed.

Logical allows logical operations to be carried out bit by bit between two registers, the result being placed in a third register. The operations allowed are AND, OR and EXCLUSIVE OR. It is also possible to NOT the contents of a single register.

Shift allows the contents of a register to be shifted by a number of places indicated in the micro-instruction. The contents can be shifted to the left or right using cyclic, logical and arithmetic techniques.

Decoder is a special instruction which allows that part of a register to be examined from which it is possible to deduce which machine instruction is to be obeyed. It is the last micro-instruction of the fetch sequence before the appropriate sequence can be initiated.

The logical and shift micro-instructions will need to comply with the sign convention used by the simulated computer. The simulator supports the use of sign and magnitude, one's complement and two's complement sign conventions.

A.2.2.3 *Output from the simulator*

The simulator produces several different types of output. First, there is information pertaining to errors encountered during the definition of the simulated computer. If any errors are encountered, the execution phase of the simulator will be omitted, because there will be an incomplete definition of the computer to be simulated. Secondly, the definition of the computer is printed, and any errors are interspersed in this output. Finally output from the execution of the program in the simulated computer is printed. This always includes the initial and final state of the computer. Information is printed either after every micro-instruction or after every machine instruction. In either case each machine instruction is followed by an indication of how long it took to execute that instruction. The output information is terminated by an indication of how long the program took to execute in the simulated computer.

A2.3 Error handling

Errors are generated in both the execution and definition phases. Definition errors are usually caused by misspelt names and incorrectly formatted data. Those procedures which might generate errors have an integer parameter so that when they are called, each instance having a different value, that number can be used to indicate which error message, if required, is to be produced. The error message is produced by a call to an error handling procedure. This mechanism ensures that all errors are found and, further, the messages are produced next to the data which caused the error.

A2.4 Implementation

The simulator was implemented on an IBM 370/135 having half a megabyte of memory. The simulator written in Pascal occupies some 1600 lines of code. This compiles into 75K bytes of code. When used in a compile load and go environment it takes about 4 minutes to process the simulation of a 16 bit, 16 function computer using a program of some 80 executed machine operations. This simulation requires a partition of 256K. When a previously compiled version of the simulator is used, the execution time is reduced to less than 1 minute. The output from such a simulation is about 80 pages.

A2.5 Use of the simulator in a teaching environment

The simulator can be used in two different ways: by students using previously defined computers where they are required to write programs for these predefined computers, and by the students defining their own particular architecture and exploring it by writing programs for it.

A2.6 Predefined computers

The use of predefined computers in the early stage of a course has two advantages. The preparation of definitions of computer architectures is non-trivial and students at the outset of a course do not have the expertise to develop their own definitions. In the early stages of a course it is desirable for them to become familiar with the use of several different types of computers. This can be done effectively if definitions of the different types already exist which demonstrate the particular architectural details necessary for the development of the subject. By examining the output from the simulator, which contains the details of the state of the computer for each machine instruction or, alternatively each micro-instruction, it is possible for the students to appreciate more fully what is going on, especially with respect to the micro-instruction set and sequences.

Computers which have been predefined are: a simple one address teaching machine, a one address machine with indirect addressing and indexing, a two address machine, and a simple stack machine (see Problems 5.10 onwards in Chapter 5). Work is going on to produce definitions of computers such as HP21MX, IBM 370 and a ZILOG microprocessor.

The following are examples of the instruction sets for some of the predefined computers.

A2.6.1 *A one address machine with indirect addressing and indexing*

Structure of Machine Instruction
4 function bits, 1 index bit, 1 indirect bit, 10 address bits
left to right within the word.

Registers Available for Use   1 accumulator
    1 index register

The following notation is used:

n	an address in store	
l	a numeric literal	
i	index register	$\begin{cases} 1 \text{ in use} \\ 0 \text{ not in use} \end{cases}$
a	addressing	$\begin{cases} 0 \text{ direct} \\ 1 \text{ indirect} \end{cases}$

Instruction Set

Number	Mnemonic	Function
0	HALT	stops computer
1	LDA n,i,a	acc = (n + (i))
2	STA n,i,a	(n + (i)) = acc
3	LDI n,0,a	i = (n)
4	STI n,0,a	n = (i)
5	ADD n,i,a	acc = acc + (n + (i))
6	SUB n,i,a	acc = acc − (n + (i))
7	INP 0,0,0	acc = input
8	OUT 0,0,0	output = acc
9	JMP n,0,a	pc = n
10	JMA n,0,a	if acc < 0 pc = n
11	SRJ n,0,a	acc = (pc) pc = n
12	CRAL 1,0,0	cyclically shift acc left l places
13	CRAR 1,0,0	cyclically shift acc right l places
14	DECI 1,0,0	i = i − 1 if i = 0 pc = 1
15	ARAR 1,0,0	arithmetically shift acc right l places

Processing Times

Memory read/write	300 ns
AU operation	100 ns

Index AU (also indirect)	30 ns
Register transfer	20 ns

A2.6.2 *A simple stack machine*

Structure of Machine Instructions
4 function bits, 12 address bits, left to right, within the word.
Registers in Use
Registers A and B hold the top two elements of the stack. The rest of the stack is in main memory with register SP containing the stack pointer.
Instruction Set
Note: m(sp) = contents of memory indicated by sp

Number	Mnemonic	Function
0	HALT	stops computer
1	PUSH	sp = sp + 1, m(sp) = B, B = A
2	POP	A = B, B = m(sp), sp = sp − 1
3	SWAP	Z = B, B = A, A = Z
4	ADD	A = A + B, B = m(sp), sp = sp − 1
5	SUB	A = A − B, B = m(sp), sp = sp − 1
6	MPY	A = A × B, B = m(sp), sp = sp − 1
7	DIV	A = A/B, B = m(sp), sp = sp − 1
8	INP	A = input
9	OUT	output = A
10	JMP n	pc = n
11	JMA n	if A < 0 pc = n
12	LDA n	A = (n)
13	STA n	n = A

Processing Times

memory (stack) read/write	300 ns
ADD SUB SP addition	100 ns
MPY DIV	500 ns
register transfer	20 ns

A2.7 Self-defined computers

The use of the simulator by users to define their own architecture is limited only by the amount of time they have available. They are able to construct machines of hypothetical architecture and to examine the ease (or lack of it) with which that machine can be programmed. In particular, they can see the effect of different speeds of register transfer or arithmetic facilities as they are felt in executing a program. The effect on speed of using direct or indirect addressing can be seen very easily.

The output of the time to execute is one of the most useful aspects of the simulator because it gives the user an indication of the efficiency of his architecture. Using the same delay on hardware units and functions, different architectures will yield different execution times. (At this level, architecture means the transfer paths that are provided and the amount of parallelism introduced.)

Index

The starred page numbers indicate the main explanatory introduction for those items which are referenced more than once.